Toolcare

BTCV is the UK's largest practical
conservation charity. We support the activities of more
than 85,000 volunteers every year, who take part in
projects and come from all sections of the community to
do practical conservation, both in the UK and worldwide.
BTCV runs a programme of Developing Skills training
courses, many of which are designed to help people put
the theory contained in the Practical Handbook series into
practice. For information about any of BTCV's
volunteering opportunities, please contact:

BTCV, 36 St Mary's Street, Wallingford,
Oxfordshire OX10 0EU

Other titles in BTCV's
Practical Handbook series:

Dry Stone Walling

Fencing

Footpaths

Hedging

Sand Dunes

Trees and Aftercare

Waterways and Wetlands

Woodlands

The Urban Handbook

To order any of these, or for details of other BTCV
publications and merchandise, please contact:

BTCV Enterprises Ltd.,
Conservation Centre, Balby Road,
Doncaster DN4 0RH.
Tel: 01302 572200 or buy
online at www.btcv.org

Toolcare

a maintenance and workshop manual

edited by Elizabeth Agate

BTCV acknowledges with thanks the help it has received in producing this publication from the following people: Andrew Brown, Mick Coad, Dave Coleman, Allan Cook, Dan England, Simon Feathers, Patrick Hardiman, George Manley, Michael Preston, Paul Redway, Doug Spark, Andy Stokes, Tony Stoneley, Ian Wallace & Nigel Watson.

ISBN   0 946752 24 9

Edited & Illustrated by Elizabeth Agate

First published in 1991, revised 1995 and 2000

1 3 5 7 9 8 6 4 2

Typeset in Palatino 9.5/12pt
Text printed on recycled paper by Watkiss Studios Ltd., Biggleswade
Published by BTCV, 36 St. Mary's Street, Wallingford OX10 0EU
Registered charity No. 261009

Contents

Foreword

This manual is intended for use by groups of people involved in practical conservation work, and is based on the experience gained over many years by the British Trust for Conservation Volunteers. Its purpose is to give guidance on the storage, maintenance and repair of tools and equipment used in conservation work, together with advice on the setting up of workshops and toolstores.

Chapters 1-4 deal with the planning, fitting out and organisation of a workshop and toolstore, and are of particular relevance to the larger conservation groups and other organisations. Chapters 5-7 describe in detail how to repair the full range of field tools. Advice is also given on the repair of workshop tools, where relevant.

The manual is designed to open flat so that it can be laid on the workshop bench, or stood in a Perspex book holder.

As in all things, opinions will differ on the best way of solving a problem, and tool storage and repair is no exception. The methods recommended in this manual are those which BTCV have found by experience to be best, but other methods are not precluded.

Dimensions are given in metric, with imperial equivalents in brackets.

BTCV Enterprises Ltd. supply a wide range of tools and equipment, from basic gardening and building tools to specialist equipment for conservation work. A range of industrial quality power and workshop tools are also available. For details BTCV Enterprises Ltd, Conservation Centre, Balby Road, Balby, Doncaster DN4 0RH. Telephone 01302 572200 or buy online at www.btcv.org.

1　Planning a workshop and toolstore

Thinking ahead

The single most important thing to keep in mind when starting to plan your workshop and toolstore is don't rush. You may have to live with a mistake for a long time if you do! Talk and plan with other members of your group. Look around your local area and talk to people who may be able to give you guidance and practical help.

Keep in mind two points: storage and expansion.

Storage

If you don't plan for adequate storage space now, then bench surfaces have a nasty habit of turning into shelves. You will be forever clearing away odd bits and pieces just to get at a work surface. You'll find that new volunteers will be put off by what will appear as an untidy pile of odds and ends. As a result they will be reluctant to become involved with tool maintenance or van loading. You will also be forever looking for things because somebody else will have moved them to find work space!

Expansion

The chances are that you will have to live with the space you acquire for some time. Look at the conservation projects you run now, and also those you hope to run in the future. You may well attract larger numbers of volunteers and start different types of projects to those you are currently running. This will mean more and different types of tools, a bigger storage area, and more broken tools waiting to be mended. Hopefully it will also mean more volunteers trying to find room around the workbenches.

Expansion could well mean a change in how you use the area. You may be running things on your own at the moment, mending tools as and when you can, and van loading may be something you do half an hour before you leave. Eventually you may envisage a regular evening or weekend session packing or repairing tools. This will involve you in training people who are not familiar with using workshop tools. You may have to set up a routine for repair and return of tools to the main storage area; you will certainly need more workbenches than you have now. So think carefully how you want the workshop to run, and how it fits in with your overall programme. This will in turn greatly affect the list of requirements which you draw up (p8).

Premises

You may well have no choice of the premises for your workshop and toolstore, but if you are starting from scratch, consider the following points when looking for premises. Whatever the event, you will probably have to settle for something which is less than ideal!

Location

If your base is in a town or city, a location near public transport will avoid your volunteers having any excuses for not turning up. In rural areas public transport is unlikely to be a relevant factor, but somewhere fairly central to your catchment area is likely to be best.

Access and parking

The ideal situation is to have both workshop and toolstore on the ground floor of a building, with direct access through wide doors to ample parking space outside. Loading and unloading tools is very much easier if you can reverse the van right up to the toolstore door (p8). Also consider parking for volunteers' cars and bikes. One sure way of falling out with any near neighbours is by infringing on their perceived parking rights!

Planning control

At an early stage you should check with the local planning authority that there are no controls over using the premises for a workshop and toolstore. You will probably need planning permission to make any external changes, such as to put in a larger door.

Noise

Depending on the nearness of neighbours, you may need to consider the effect on good relations of both noise from the workshop and from vehicles. Various measures can be taken (p10) to reduce the amount of noise heard outside the workshop. The noise of vehicles and occupants coming and going is largely a matter of consideration for others.

Security

This is a problem for both rural and urban premises. Don't consider anywhere that cannot be made secure, and take extra measures as necessary (p8)

Lease

If taking out a lease, you will probably need to get legal advice. If the arrangement is of a more informal nature, perhaps using a member's garage or a farm building, at least come to a friendly agreement first, written if possible. This should cover matters such as payment for electricity used, repair of any damage, contents insurance, reinstatement (i.e. putting things back as they were) and the period of any 'notice to quit'.

Finding premises

Presuming you have any choice, how does one go about finding premises? The first step is to ask members of the group, and get them to follow up any contacts they may have. Other organisations in the conservation field may also be able to help, including the countryside service or parks department of the local authority. Then look through advertisements in local newspapers, and enquire at estate agents. You may strike lucky by simply looking around the area you are interested in and making enquiries about any empty property.

List of requirements

Once possible premises have been found, the following points need considering:

a Power supply (p11).

b Water supply (p12).

c Number of benches. Base this on the number of people you have at training sessions, or hope to have. There should be a bench space for each person (p12).

d Number of workshop tools (p13).

e Specialist benches e.g. chainsaw, crosscut or circular saw, grinders etc.

f Storage space for fieldwork tools and equipment (pp21-27).

g Storage space for broken tools and new handles.

h Storage space for project materials. In most cases, clients provide all materials on site, but some groups may have supplies of their own materials, such as timber for stiles.

i Shelf or desk for administration e.g. tool lists, records, files, notice board, lost property.

j Safe storage for petrol, Calor gas and herbicides (p16).

Structural alterations

Where tenancy of the building and funds allow, some structural alterations may help you make the best of the space you have acquired. Any structural alterations should be carried out by competent people.

Access

To speed loading and unloading of tools, make sure that vans can be reversed as close as possible to the toolstore door. If there is a pavement outside the door, you can put down temporary wooden ramps so that the van can be reversed up onto the pavement, so long as you do not cause an obstruction.

Double doors or a single wide door that allow two people to pass are useful during loading and unloading sessions, and also for manoeuvring any large items of equipment such as work benches. Planning permission may be needed to alter the door. Most demolition yards should have a good selection of doors, and you may be able to get one complete with frame.

Exits from the toolstore and workshop should be marked as such and kept clear and well lit at all times. Fire extinguishers should be provided (p19).

Security

Fit or replace door locks as necessary. Each external door should have a security deadlock, which is a lock that can only be opened or closed with a key. Double

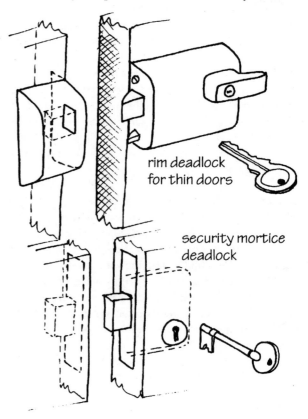

rim deadlock for thin doors

security mortice deadlock

doors should have one door with bolts, and the other with a deadlock. Night latch locks, which can be opened from the inside without a key, are not sufficiently secure. A thief gaining access through a window can then open the door from the inside for an easy getaway. Night latch locks can also be easily opened by breaking an adjacent window and reaching through. Make sure you know exactly what size and combination of lock and handle you need before purchasing, as they are available in a bewildering selection. Security deadlocks are of two basic types: either a mortice lock which fits into the thickness of the door, or a rim lock for thinner doors which is screwed onto the face of the door. Mortice locks are the more secure.

Window locks for virtually all types of windows, including skylights, are available from DIY stores, and are well worth fitting.

Natural light

The workshop area should receive a reasonable amount of natural light, as this is the best light under which to work. If considering putting in extra windows, remember that this will mean less wall space for storage, and increased security risk. Skylights are a useful way of getting more light into a room without loss of wall space, and also give valuable overhead light so that workbenches can be placed centrally (p12). Velux roof windows are easy to fix to tiled or corrugated roofs, and may not require planning permission (except on a listed building), but are rather costly. Windows are readily available from demolition yards, or free for the asking where replacement windows are being fitted. Check that the frames are sound.

Painting the walls white will make the most of the available light, and make wall-hung tools and racks easy to see.

Ventilation

For workshop areas, this should be considered at the same time as natural light. Under Building Standards, any habitable room must have opening windows with a total area equal to at least one twentieth of the floor area. Although most workshops would not be classed as habitable, this does give a guide to the minimum ventilation needed. Where a lot of dust is being created, extra ventilation will be needed. Extractor fans are available which can be fitted either vertically or horizontally.

You must also consider ventilation for the toolstore, to prevent the build up of humid air which will speed deterioration of tools, wellies, tents, ropes and so on. Ventilation is also important if storing LPG or petrol (p16). If the toolstore needs to be locked up for most of the time, make sure the ventilation is burglar-proof.

Apart from windows, the various options for increased ventilation include extractor fans in external walls, internal windows or openings which ventilate into other parts of the building, and vents fitted into wooden floors, disused chimneys and roof spaces.

Division of area

The ideal is to have separate but adjacent rooms for the toolstore and workshop, with an outside door and direct vehicle access. You would normally want the toolstore nearest to the outside door, to minimise the distance tools have to be carried. At all costs avoid the arrangement where you have to walk through the workshop to reach the toolstore. Not only will tools inevitably get dumped in the workshop, but workshop tools will tend to disappear out on projects. The workshop should have its own internal door which can be locked.

If the available area is divided between different floors, you would normally have the toolstore on the ground floor for ease of access. However, other factors such as natural light, power and water supply or the size of the rooms may dictate otherwise.

In deciding the division of floor space between toolstore and workshop, you need to think about how your group works. If you run training sessions on workshop skills you will need enough room for several workbenches, or for a very large central bench around which several people can work. If on the other hand the group does not run training sessions but has only one or two people who take responsibility for all tool maintenance, you can manage with a much smaller area.

Whatever size your toolstore, you will find that tools apparently expand to fill it. This is because with more space you can get away with being less tidy, and also with being less ruthless about clearing out the odds and ends that accumulate. The same, of course, applies to a workshop, office or anywhere else. In a small space you have to be tidy and organised. With proper racks and shelves (pp21-27), a large number of tools can be stored in a surprisingly small area. An oddly shaped toolstore can be an advantage as this provides lots of wall space and corners for storage. A single open space will need to be provided with freestanding racks, shelves and so on to make the most of the space available.

If you are faced with a single area for both workshop and toolstore, you may need to put up a partition. Unless your group does a large amount of training, a division of about one third workshop to two thirds toolstore should be about right, but each situation needs assessing individually. Remember also that you may want to heat the workshop (p11) if you intend working in it during the winter, and this can be done much more efficiently in a smaller area.

The simplest type of partition to erect is of wooden studwork faced with plasterboard. Consult any good DIY book for details. Although properly constructed stud partitions can take a fair amount of weight, beware of overloading them with shelves or racks of very heavy items. Fixings for shelves must always be made to the upright studs, not to the horizontals or the building boards. If in any doubt, it is reccomended that a competent contractor is consulted.

Windows can be incorporated into stud partitions, providing 'borrowed light' and ventilation for the darker room. Stud partitions can easily be removed if the requirements for space change, and re-use of most of the materials should be possible.

Where the lease allows, and floor conditions are appropriate, a stronger partition could be made of concrete blocks, rendered and painted. This would also be more sound-proof than a stud partition, which may be useful in some circumstances, and can take a greater load from shelves or racks.

Floors

Wooden floors, either on ground or upper levels, should be checked to make sure they are in sufficiently sound condition to take the loads you intend putting on them. This should be done before any lease is signed, as repair is a major undertaking. Wooden floors at ground level can become rotten if there is no damp-proof membrane, and rot may not be immediately obvious. If there is any doubt, get a building surveyor to check.

Solid concrete floors should be fairly trouble free, though damp can be a problem. The effects of damp can be lessened by painting the floor with a damp sealer. Small holes and irregularities can be levelled by first applying a PVA compound and then filling it with a 1:3 cement-sand mortar with PVA added. Larger irregularities may just have to be lived with, as they are difficult to level without laying a new screed over the entire floor. Self-levelling cement can be used in some situations, but needs to then be itself protected with a floor covering. Note that some machines, such as lathes, must be mounted on perfectly level floors.

Concrete floors are cold to stand on, and do nothing to deaden sound, but any form of covering is usually too expensive. Vinyl on workshop floors tends to get swarf (tiny slivers of metal produced during metalworking) embedded into it. Concrete floors can be improved in appearance and made easier to keep clean by sealing and painting with a concrete paint.

Noise reduction

Apart from the noise of vehicles and over enthusiastic volunteers, the main source of noise from a workshop is likely to be from machinery and power tools. The first step in noise reduction is to make sure that machinery is running properly and that all parts are securely fastened, so that vibration is reduced. Vibration isolators can be fitted between the mounting points of a machine and the operating surface. Commercial vibration isolators, made of rubber sandwiched in metal, are available, and the machine manufacturer should be able to advise on the most suitable type. Otherwise, pads of cork or felt can be used, although these will deteriorate with age and exposure to oil. Special pads of dense rubber are available from car parts suppliers, which can be stuck onto metal surfaces to reduce vibration and noise.

Noise reduction measures include both reducing noise within the room by providing materials that absorb sound, and by insulating to reduce noise reaching the outside. Low density materials such as polystyrene which have high absorbency do not insulate against noise transmission. The best materials for insulation and absorption of sound have a high density and low stiffness. Any very stiff material such as metal can be improved by backing with a layer of mastic, plasterboard or mineral wool.

Various materials can be used to line walls and ceilings to absorb and reflect sound, including polystyrene, fibreglass insulation, and even materials such as foam, thick fabrics, carpeting and egg-trays. A few old armchairs placed in the room can reduce sound in more ways that one! Unfortunately, most of these materials constitute a major fire-risk. Probably the best material to use is mineral wool or rolls of fibreglass of the type used for heat insulation, attached behind hardboard, pegboard or perforated sheet metal. Various insulating sheet materials are also available from building suppliers. It may be worth insulating the ceiling or roof anyway to prevent heat loss from the building.

Another technique is to hang panels of absorbent material vertically from the ceiling. The noise is reflected from one panel to another and thus absorbed.

Polystyrene must not be used in tool stores or workshops.

2 Fitting out a workshop and toolstore

Having made any structural changes necessary, you can now start laying on services and fitting out the workshop and toolstore.

There will be many local resources in your area for materials and guidance. Visit railway yards for old sleepers, and building demolition sites and demolition yards for all sorts of materials. Look in the local paper for farm and country house auctions. These can be a cheap source of tools as well as other materials. Talk to your local timber merchants and get an idea of the going rate for materials. You will then be in a better position for judging whether auction prices are worthwhile. Advertise in your group newsletter and visit your volunteer bureau. Visit other local groups and BTCV regional workshops and toolstores, schools workshops and college facilities.

Services

Electricity

The following is intended for guidance only. Any electrical work must be carried out by a qualified electrician.

The workshop, toolstore, and all passages and stairs must have adequate lighting. External lighting is very useful for van loading and unloading during the winter months. Fluorescent tubes are recommended for internal lighting as they have a longer life, give more than twice as much light as tungsten bulbs of the same wattage, and are cheaper to run. 'Daylight' tubes give the best light for workshops. In choosing the number and length of fluorescent tubes for a room, you should allow 10 watts/m² of floor area to be lit. Spotlighting for workbenches may also be useful. This can be provided by an Anglepoise type lamp either attached to the wall or to a moveable bracket, and run off the power circuit. Grinders, drill stands and other fixed power equipment should each have their own spotlight. The invisible flickering of fluorescent light is dangerous with very fast rotating machinery, as it has a 'freezing' effect.

Don't skimp on lighting in the toolstore, as people are much more likely to put tools away neatly if they can see what they're doing. Make sure any recesses or odd corners are well lit, as these are especially useful for tool storage.

You will need sufficient power points in the workshop for the power tools you intend to use, plus a few extra for additional lighting, heat and so on. It is better to have too many, than to risk the dangers of adaptors and trailing extension leads. Power to a central bench should be supplied by cabling brought under the floor and through the underside of the bench, and not by dangling overhead cabling. On solid floors, cabling should be brought through a plastic conduit laid into a channel in the floor. If this is not practical, fix a stout wooden pillar from the bench top to the ceiling and bring the cabling overhead and then down, clipped to the pillar. Put pads of cork or similar material (p10) at the base and top of the pillar to reduce sound transmission from bench to ceiling.

The electrical system for the building should be fitted with mini circuit breakers and individual power tools protected by a residual current device (RCD), operating at 30mA in 0.4 seconds, which will instantly cut off the supply in the event of an earth fault.

Heating

The workshop may need some form of heating to make it comfortable for use during the winter months. Heating is not essential in the toolstore, but where available, a low degree of heat can be useful in promoting a dry atmosphere to combat rusting of tools, and prevent dampness and mould in tents, hessian sacks, ropes and so on. However, an excessively dry atmosphere will cause tool handles to shrink and warp.

Electricity is the safest form of heating for a workshop, as there are no naked flames. It is also a dry heat, which is kindest to tools. However, it is likely to be the most expensive, and is not very efficient for rapid heating of a large area. As it uses a large amount of power, it may cause overloading when electric power equipment is also being used. Gas and solid fuel both cause condensation on cold surfaces, which can cause rusting of metal tools. Ensure adequate ventilation to counteract this. Store chemicals, petrol and gas well away from any source of heating (p16).

Calor gas heaters, give very rapid heat and can heat a surprisingly large area. However they do cause considerable condensation so good ventilation is required. They also give off carbon monoxide, and attention must be paid to their maintenance. Choose the size appropriate for the area you need to heat.

The only electrical heater likely to be of use in a workshop is a large fan heater, which can be directed towards the work area when conditions become too cold.

Wood burning stoves heat up quicker than might be expected, and most conservation groups will have no trouble supplying their own fuel. A safe storage area for fuel will be required. Never be tempted to burn offcuts of creosoted or CCA (copper chrome arsenate) treated timber, as the former burns very fiercely, and both give off noxious fumes. Stoves are very expensive to buy new, but should be available second-hand at a more reasonable price. You may find by asking around that someone has one not currently in use that they will loan you. The workshop will need to have an existing chimney, and you will need a section or two of flue, available from stove suppliers, which can be fitted into a fire-screen. The screen can be easily made out of a piece of metal sheeting, and fixed in position with fire cement. An airer or rack placed above, though not directly over, a stove is a useful place for drying wet clothing and equipment. Note that any stove used in a smoke-controlled zone must be of a type approved for that use. Check with supplier.

Water

The workshop should have a water supply and sink for washing hands. An outside tap over a drain is very useful for washing tools and equipment. An alternative is simply to fit a water butt with a tap to a downpipe from the roof. This should be adequately replenished during times when tools are at their muddiest.

Emergency information

Any toolstore or workshop should have a First Aid kit, separate from those used for projects, which is never removed. The location of this must be displayed. Other information which should be displayed includes the location of the nearest phone, the locations of the stop taps for water and gas, and the electricity cut off switch. All emergency exits must be signed and the fire extinguishers clearly marked.

Workshop layout

Each situation will be different, but there are a few general points to note:

a Make a clear gangway down the centre of the workshop or around the central benches. The gangways should be kept clear of tools and other materials and can be defined by painted yellow lines on the floor.

b If there is room, align the benches so that the operators are clear of the gangways. One arrangement is to have benches set diagonally as shown in the diagram, so that each operator has his or her own work space. If there is not enough room for this arrangement, at least make sure that gangways are wide enough for people to walk past operators without knocking into them.

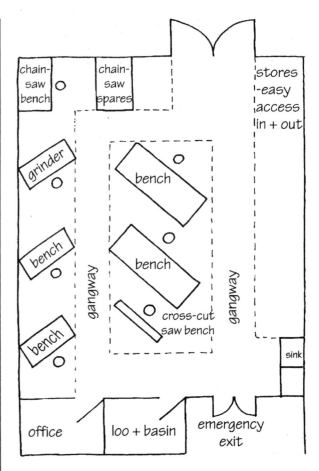

○ operator
all operators clear of gangways

c The storage area for broken or mended tools and spares is best sited near the door, to give easy access.

d Natural light gives the best light for working under, so site benches to take advantage of this. A wide bench with room for an operator either side, or two narrow benches back to back, can be sited end on to a window, so that both operators can benefit from natural light.

e A large central bench makes efficient use of space and is a sociable way of running training and workshop sessions. The BTCV London workshop has a central bench 2.5m (8') by 1.6m (5') with six vices.

f Position grinders so that grit is thrown towards a blank wall and away from other operators.

g Try to keep the chainsaw bench separate from the general benches so it is less likely to get used for other purposes, and provide sufficient lockable storage space for chainsaw spares and accessories.

General purpose benches

A bench for a single operator need only be 600mm (2') wide. Benches wider than this tend to accumulate odds and ends along the back which are better stored away. For most of the work described in this manual, a 900mm (3') wide bench gives adequate space for an operator on either side.

Height will be a matter of personal preference, but 860mm (34") to 910mm (36") should suit most people. One or two benches can be made lower, at 810mm (32") to 860mm (34"), to suit shorter people. To find the correct height for yourself, stand erect with the forearm at right angles to the body, and the wrist limp. The finger tips are at the ideal height.

A bench up to 1.8m (6') long can have two pairs of legs of 75 x 75mm (3 x 3"), with rails of the same size. A longer bench will need three pairs of legs of 100 x 100mm (4 x 4") with rails of 100 x 75mm (4 x 3"). The design below shows a bench with tool well, but if not required, a simple flat top can be fitted. If possible the top should be hardwood. Otherwise, use two layers of 18mm (3/4") blockboard glued and screwed together, covered with a sheet of hardboard which can be replaced when worn. Old solid core flush doors also make useful worktops. For metalworking, 25mm (1") chipboard topped with galvanised plate can be used.

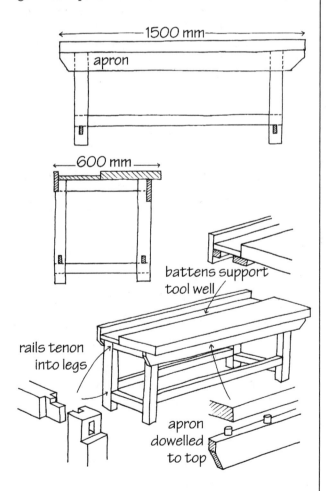

The apron is important in the construction of the bench as it gives rigidity, especially when lengthwise loads are being applied. The worktop should be fitted from un-derneath with screws counterbored into the rails, to avoid having metal exposed on the worktop. Cupboards or shelves can be fitted underneath the bench as required.

Dexion can be used to make any size of bench. The square bench shown would be suitable for mounting a grinder. Dexion is available from suppliers of shelving and racking systems.

Dexion bench with blockboard top

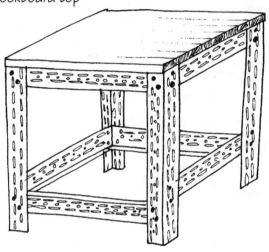

Workshop tools

List of requirements

A properly equipped workshop should include the tools listed below, many of which are available from BTCV Enterprises Ltd. Other items should be obtainable locally from good ironmongers and tools suppliers (see 'Tools' listings in Yellow Pages). Classified advertisements in woodworking and other trade magazines are also worth looking through.

Any bench mounted grindstone, operating at high speeds, must comply with the Provision and Use of Work Equipment Regulations 1998. The poster outlining these regulations must be displayed. The grindstone must be attached to a residual current device (RCD), and it must only be used by competent people. The wheels may only be changed by a person who has undergone an approved course for this, and only this person is allowed to adjust the rest.

Tools – general

Vice (metalwork). 105mm (4.25") or 125mm (5") vices with quick release jaws are recommended. Plastic inserts are available which fit onto the jaws and prevent damage to material being held in the vice.

Anvil. This can be improvised from any suitable heavy piece of steel, and should be attached to the workbench.

Hand or electric drill. A hammer action electric drill is useful for drilling into walls when fitting out the workshop and toolstore.

Drill bits. Carbon steel or high speed steel (HSS) bits, in a selection of sizes from 3-10mm.

Ball pein hammers, 340g (12oz) and 680g (1.5lb).

Cross pein hammer, 340g (12oz).

Pin hammer, 110g (3.5oz).

Lump hammer, 1360g (3lb).

Screwdrivers, flat and cross-headed (see below).

Spanners, open-ended and ring, or combination type.

Pliers

Saws, tenon, panel, and ripsaw.

Hacksaw

Claw hammers, 455g (16oz) and 570g (20oz).

Saw set, to set teeth when sharpening saws.

Saw set (heavy duty), for scrub cutter and crosscut saws.

Cold chisels

Mallet, wooden, rubber or plastic.

Glass-paper, in coarse, medium and fine grades. Also silicon carbide (wet and dry) paper in selection of grades.

Oils. Light oil such as '3 in 1' for use with oilstones. Vegetable oil for general oiling of tool heads. This becomes sticky with age, so do not buy in large quantities. Linseed oil for tool handles.

Rags

Safety goggles, manufactured to BS: 2092.

Ear defenders (either plugs or muffs).

Wire brush

Ruler, preferably metal.

Pencils, 2B.

Tools – sharpening

Machine sandstone (vertical whetstone grinder). A 60rpm machine is suitable, being slow and working at a low temperature, so it will not ruin the temper of the tool head. The grinding wheel is suspended in a reservoir of water. A machine sandstone will cope with most grinding jobs, and is the machine to choose if only one grinding machine is to be purchased. It will however make slow work of grinding a badly damaged edge, such as on an axe, which is easier done on a bench grinder.

Bench grinder. This normally has one coarse and one fine grinding wheel. A grinder with 150mm (6") wheels is suitable. The bench grinder works at a higher speed than a machine sandstone, and therefore greater care and skill is needed in its use, to avoid hollow grinding or damaging the temper of the tool head. Combination machines are available, which include a water-cooled sandstone and a high-speed dry grinding wheel.

Angle grinder. A hand-held power tool which can be used with a selection of grinding and cutting discs, or with abrasives on a rubber backing pad. Various models are available, with "no load" speeds of between 6,500 and 12,000 rpm, of which the lower speed is suitable. Great care is needed in their use, both for operator safety, and to avoid damage or overheating of the tool edge.

Files. Flat and half-round files in various sizes and cuts will be necessary. Single-cut files with teeth arranged in single diagonal rows are best for hard metals. Rasp-cut files are best for soft metals. 200-250mm (8-10") coarse mill files with round edges are recommended for most jobs.

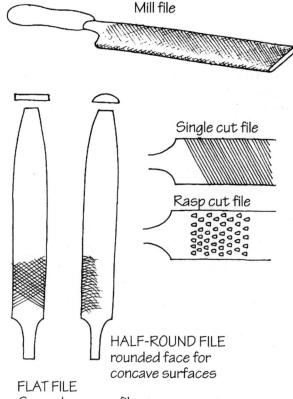

Mill file

Single cut file

Rasp cut file

HALF-ROUND FILE
rounded face for
concave surfaces

FLAT FILE
General purpose file

Oil stones, coarse and fine. An alternative is to have a combination stone, which is coarse on one side and fine on the other. One of the best such stones is the 'India', made from aluminium oxide (Aloxite). It should be used with a light oil such as '3 in 1'. If used properly, these stones will last for many years use, without ever any need for truing (rubbing flat).

Axe stone. This sharpening stone has one medium side and one fine side.

Canoe stone. A medium stone for sharpening billhooks and slashers.

Cigar stone. A coarse stone for sharpening curved tools such as scythes and grasshooks, and for honing in the field during use.

Note however that the shape of the stone does not always determine its grade or grit size, and if purchasing by post it is worth checking the grade before ordering.

Tools – rehafting

Surform. For shaping handles. Spare blades are obtainable.

Spokeshaves (flat and bevelled). For shaping handles.

Draw knife. For shaping handles. Quickly removes wood without clogging.

Wood chisels

Centre punch

Blunt-ended punch. This can be improvised from an old coach bolt. An alternative is a dolly, made from a piece of hardwood (illustration on p35).

Metal wedges, selection of sizes.

Wooden wedges (p36).

Rivets. These can be made from round nails of the correct diameter.

Storage

Hand tools should be stored in purpose-built racks, preferably inside lockable cupboards. See section on storage of small tools (p25).

Power tools should be stored in accordance with the manufacturer's instructions.

Maintenance of workshop tools

All tools, whether hand or power, should be regularly maintained. This can range from an occasional wipe over with a clean oily rag for metal parts, or linseed oil for wooden parts, to a total overhaul. You should not attempt the latter unless you have the required specialist knowledge to attempt the task. This is especially important in the case of power tools.

All electrical equipment should be checked regularly and tested by a competent electrician. The frequency of this testing will vary with the item, but for very regularly used items, such as drills and extension cables, a test should be made at least annually, together with a visual check every time they are used. For less regularly used items a test no less than every five years will suffice, but a visual check should be made every time they are used. A visual check should include looking for worn or loose wires, signs of overheating, and damage to the working parts of the equipment.

The section below gives some notes on tools normally only used in the workshop. For details on maintenance and repair of fieldwork tools, see chapters 5 and 6.

Saws

After every use, saws should be lightly oiled to prevent rust on the blade. Vegetable oil is cheap and biodegradable.

Rip and panel saws should be sharpened, and reset if necessary, using saw sets and sharpening files. The files are supplied in jigs, and should be used according to the manufacturer's instructions. If your workshop does not include these tools, then rip and panel saws should be taken to a good saw doctor or hardware store for sharpening and setting.

The sharpening of tenon and dovetail saws should not be attempted in the workshop as great precision is needed. Take these to a saw doctor.

Hacksaws

Hacksaws are available in three types: tubular, solid framed and junior. All types have non-resharpenable blades. Purchase high-speed flexible blades, not stiff blades which although cheaper, go blunt quickly and can shatter. A coarse blade, with 24 teeth to the inch, is suitable for general use. When fitting a new blade, take care to fit it the correct way round, with the teeth pointing forwards.

For tubular or solid framed hacksaws the wing nut is slackened, the old blade removed and a new one fitted. Do not overtighten the wing nut or the blade will easily snap. To tension the blade, take up the slack, and then apply two full turns only. There should be a washer fitted between the wing nut and the saw frame. The junior saw has a fine blade, with 36 teeth to the inch. To replace, compress the frame to release the old blade and then fit the new one.

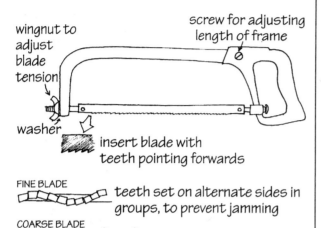

wingnut to adjust blade tension

washer

screw for adjusting length of frame

insert blade with teeth pointing forwards

FINE BLADE

teeth set on alternate sides in groups, to prevent jamming

COARSE BLADE

single teeth set alternately; every fifth tooth left straight to clear chippings away

Drills

Hand drills should have the pinions regularly greased with a standard grease. They should not be oiled, as this will attract grit when the tool is in use and shorten its working life.

Power drills should be maintained in accordance with the manufacturer's instructions.

Drill bits can be sharpened in a bit sharpener, available from DIY stores.

Screwdrivers

The screwdriver is a much abused tool. Always use one that matches the screw being driven for both size and shape of tip. If they are not matched, the result will be a screw so badly worn that it is almost impossible to remove, or a screwdriver with a badly damaged tip. The tip can be reground as for a chisel (p48), but both sides of the blade are ground to an angle, usually 15-20 degrees, and the tip is ground flat and square.

Files

Files must be sharp to be safe, and of any use. They have a limited life span and although fairly expensive, must be replaced when blunt. A sharp file bites into the metal, feeling as though it is dragging a little over the surface. A blunt file skids across the surface without biting, and could result in injury to the hand when sharpening

edged tools. Files get tiny particles of metal embedded between the teeth, a process known as pinning. This can be avoided by rubbing white chalk on the file teeth. Files can be cleaned with a wire brush. File-cleaning scratch pads are available, but excessive use of these will dull files. For stubborn dirt, use a flat piece of hardwood, about the same section as the file, with one end cut to a chisel edge. Push this across the teeth, maintaining firm pressure, and dirt will be lifted.

Files must always be used with a properly fitted handle, or there is a risk of the tang causing injury to the wrist and forearm. A file cuts on the forward stroke only, and should be lifted off on the return stroke. Rubbing it back and forth will quickly cause it to become blunt.

hardwood

lifts dirt

Storage of chemicals and petrol

The following sections give guidelines for the storage of chemicals, petrol and gas, with information on statutory regulations where relevant. In all cases try to store only the minimum amount needed, and for the shortest possible time.

Chemicals

All conservation groups will be trying to reduce the use of chemicals of all sorts, but some use is likely to be needed in the short term. Chemicals used may include herbicides, wood preservatives, masonry treatment products, paints, solvents and cleaning fluids. Under the Control of Substances Hazardous to Health Regulations 1999 (COSHH), employers and employees have to take various measures to remove any risk to health through use or exposure to such substances. Where removal is not possible, reducing or controlling exposure must be done. Voluntary groups should take similar measures to control risk. Substances hazardous to health include those labelled as very toxic, toxic, harmful, irritant or corrosive, agricultural pesticides (including herbicides) and substances with occupational exposure limits. COSHH leaflets, available free from all Health and Safety Executive Area Offices, give further details.

Few conservation groups use any of the range of approved pesticides for farmers and other professional users, partly because of the training in their use which is necessary under the Control of Pesticides Regulations 1986 (COPR). Instead, pesticides approved for amateur use, which are not subject to these regulations, can be substituted in most cases.

If using any chemical, amateur or professional, an assessment of the hazards and necessary precautions arising from them should be made available to all users. Only competent persons can use chemicals and the appropriate level of instruction in their use must be given.

The following guidelines are suggested for voluntary conservation groups:

a   Store only the minimum amount of chemicals needed, and for the shortest possible time.

b   Store chemicals in a metal cabinet or bin, which is strong enough to resist any likely accidental damage, and gives some resistance to fire.

c   Keep the cabinet or bin locked, and display warning signs on the outside.

d   The cabinet or bin should be ventilated, and should include within it a sump capable of containing any leakage up to the total capacity of the contents stored.

e   The cabinet or bin would normally be kept in the workshop. It should not be positioned in a staff room, office, human or animal food store, dwelling house or building adjoining and directly accessible from a dwelling house.

Special cabinets and bins are available from manufacturers of safety equipment (see 'Safety Equipment' listings in local Yellow Pages). Otherwise, metal office filing cupboards should be suitable, with the addition of a sump and ventilation holes.

Petrol

You are not permitted to store more than 15 litres of petrol in one place without a licence from your local Fire Authority. Petrol must always be stored in containers designed for the purpose. No container must hold more than 5 litres.

Keep the petrol containers in a non-ventilated metal cabinet or box, clearly labelled, and positioned away from an exit and possible sources of combustion, for safety reasons. Keep a suitable fire extinguisher (dry powder or carbon dioxide) nearby.

Storage of liquefied petroleum gas (LPG)

Much of the following information is from 'Storage of full and empty LPG cylinders and cartridges' (1999) published by: LPG Association, Athena Drive, Tachbrook Park, Warwick CV34 6RL.

LPG includes commercial butane, commercial propane and other mixtures defined under BS: 4250, including Calor gas. Butane is recommended for BTCV use. Propane has a higher vapour pressure at room temperature than butane, and hence requires stronger cylinders for storage. Some double burners such as the 'Dixie 2' have 'For Outside Use Only' on them, which means they are designed for propane. These should be adjusted for butane use by your local LPG dealer.

LPG is normally stored as a liquid under pressure, and any leakage may release large volumes of flammable gases. A very small proportion of these gases in air can create an explosive mixture.

LPG vapour is heavier than air and may flow along the ground or through drains and be ignited at some distance from the source of leakage. In still air vapour disperses slowly. LPG liquid can cause severe frost burns if it comes in contact with the skin.

General information on storage

Note the following:

a   LPG should preferably be stored in the open air, but where this is not possible, quantities should be restricted to that shown below in Table 2.1.

b   There must be no smoking or use of naked flames at storage points. LPG must be stored away from the workshop area where sparks may be created.

c   Refillable LPG cylinders are considered to be 'full' whatever the state of their contents, and should be stored and handled likewise. The stated weight of a cylinder refers only to the weight of the liquified gas it can contain, not the weight of the cylinder itself. For example, a 15kg cylinder is one which can contain a maximum of 15kg of liquified gas.

d   LPG should be stored away from cylinders containing other gases or hazardous substances.

e   Storage should always be at ground level, and never in cellars or basements. Storage areas must always be accessible.

f   LPG should not be stored within 2m of a drain.

g   The floor of the storage space should be compacted or paved and kept free from weeds, long grass and accumulations of combustible materials.

h   Cylinders should not be stored in vehicles.

i   Cylinders should always be stored upright, with outlet valves closed, and protective cover, cap or plug in position where supplied.

j Cylinders should never be dropped or knocked violently.

Open air storage

Quantities of between 15 and 400kg stored in the open air must be a minimum of 1m from a boundary, building or fixed ignition source.

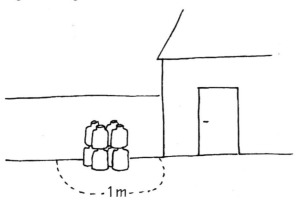

Quantities of between 15 and 400kg can be stored against a fence or wall which is not a boundary, or in the angle between two walls. They can also be stored between two wing walls, provided these walls do not exceed 2m in height and length.

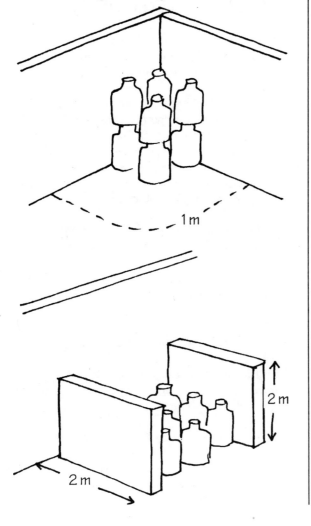

Storage in buildings

Quantities stored must not exceed those shown below. Cylinders which are in use, for example in Calor gas heaters, are exempt from the storage requirements.

Table 2.1 shows maximum storage allowance for containerised LPG in shops or offices.

Table 2.1

Building	Max LPG	Remarks
residential	15kg	Unless 60 minutes fire resisting separation is provided between the two occupancies with no direct access between, when up to 70kg may be stored.
non-residential	70kg	Not more than 5 cylinders or 20 if the maximum capacity is 3kg. No cylinder to exceed 20kg capacity.

Detection of leaks

Cylinders should be inspected regularly for leakage. Never attempt to find a leak by means of a naked flame. Leakage can be detected by sense of smell, sound of escaping gas, or condensation or frosting around the leak. Soapy water can be brushed over the suspected source, and any bubbles that form confirm the leak.

If a cylinder is found to be leaking and the leak cannot be stopped by closing the valve, inserting the bung or fitting the cap, nearby sources of ignition must be extinguished. Move the cylinder carefully to a well ventilated open space clear of drains. Leave it with the leak (presumably at the valve) uppermost, marked as faulty, with notices prohibiting smoking and other naked lights. Inform the supplier immediately. No attempt should be made by an unqualified person to dismantle or repair faulty cylinder valves.

Fire protection

For storage of less than 400kg, a 9kg dry powder extinguisher should be provided.

Do not try to fight a cylinder fire.

Compliance with the code of guidance

Compliance with the code of guidance should not be a problem for most BTCV and other groups, as few groups will need to store more than five or six 15kg cylinders at a time. However, note should be taken of the limits for storage in buildings with residential accommodation (see Table 2.1 left).

The safest place for storage is to keep the cylinders outside, if necessary in a metal cage or fenced enclosure which can be padlocked for security. A suitable cage could be made out of Weldmesh or similar material. A fenced enclosure or compound should have industrial fences 2m high, with two outward opening gates, not self-locking. Any cage or enclosure must be sited within the limits described above (p17). Contact your local supplier or regional office of Liquefied Petroleum Gas Ltd. for further advice.

Fire precautions

Fires can start anywhere, but workshops and toolstores, especially those in timber-framed buildings are a particular hazard. Note the following:

a Highly flammable liquids, including petrol, paints, solvents and pesticides, and liquified petroleum gas (Calor gas) must be safely stored (p17). Buy only what you need to minimise the need for storage.

b Keep workshops and toolstores tidy and free of rubbish, especially oily rags and paper.

c Ensure all electrical and power equipment is in safe working order.

d Provide the correct type of fire extinguishers for the likely hazards, and train staff and volunteers in their use.

e Workshops should be non-smoking areas. Provide clear notices to this effect.

The local Fire Authority may provide a free fire check of your premises and give advice on matters such as fire extinguishers, exits, alarms, signs and so on. Some authorities also hold day or half-day training courses on fire prevention.

Fire safety checks

Fire extinguishers should be checked monthly to ensure they are in their correct positions, and that they are not damaged, empty or corroded. Weight is a clear indicator of content, except for carbon dioxide extinguishers, on which the wire and lead seal should be intact. Partly used extinguishers should always be refilled and checked by the supplier. All extinguishers should be checked annually by the suppliers and marked as having been done.

Beware of the following hazards, and take action to remedy them.

a Oil or grease that has dripped onto the floor, and then been covered with sawdust, making a combustible mixture.
Clean up any accidental spillage of oil, grease or other flammable substances immediately, and dispose of the waste to an external rubbish collection point. Disposal of oil or chemicals should be checked with the local Environmental Health Department. Provide drip trays where necessary. Dirty oil and other liquids can be put into an old oil can for disposal.

b Electric cables trailing in oil or chemicals.
Avoid any trailing cables, and clean up spillages of oil or chemicals.

c Water running down walls into electrical sockets.
Turn off the electricity supply at the mains, and do not switch on until action has been taken to remedy water leaks. Check sockets for corrosion and condensation.

d Motor housings and ventilation slots clogged with dust and fluff. Electrical equipment that smells. Keep all electrical and other power equipment clean and in proper working order.

e Piles of oily rags, paper and other rubbish.
Remove rubbish regularly. Store only a few oily rags, and keep these in a metal container with lid. Dispose of oily rags when soiled.

Fire alarms

Battery operated smoke detectors are cheap and readily available, and are well worth installing in all premises. Most fires produce appreciable smoke before they produce heat; thus smoke detectors are usually more effective than heat detectors, as well as being cheaper. Instructions on the best places to install alarms are included with the fitting instructions.

Fire extinguishers

It is very important that the correct type of extinguishers are installed for the type of fire likely to be encountered. Suppliers of fire extinguishing equipment will advise on what you need, and where they should be positioned in the building.

All new fire extinguishers are red. They have a coloured panel to indicate their contents, which could be:

Water (Red panel). Water extinguishers should be used on fires of wood, paper and textiles. They must not be used on electrical fires because of the danger of electrocution. Even if the electrical appliance is switched off, the use of water can make it dangerous when it is switched back on. Water should not be used on flammable liquid fires.

Foam (Cream panel). Foam is suitable for 'contained' flammable liquids in open vessels, for example in open drums, tanks and drip trays.

Foam is water based, and so should not be used on electrical fires.

Dry Powder (Blue panel). For use on flammable liquids that are either 'contained' or free flowing, and on electrical fires.

Carbon Dioxide (Black panel). Similar uses to dry powder, but with less messy results, so may be preferable for indoor use. Can be used to penetrate into motor casings via ventilation slots, and also switchboxes and vehicle engines. The extinguisher makes a loud noise when discharged.

All fire extinguishers should be wall-mounted about 1m off the floor, and an appropriate safety sign displayed above which informs on the type of extinguisher available.

3 Storage

General points

Note the following:

a Tools must be stored safely, normally with the heads downwards. There must be no danger of tools being knocked by people walking past, or of hanging tools falling onto people.

b Make sure tools are put in a position where everyone can reach them safely, whatever their height or strength. Provide proper 'hop-ups' or sturdy steps as necessary for people to reach higher racks. Remember that back injury is very likely if you have to reach over something to lift a heavy tool.

c Store tools in such a way that they are easy to count, and it is easy to see if any are missing.

d Store tools so that they are dry, preferably raised off the floor. Store them in such a way that they won't be damaged in storage, nor while putting them away or getting them out.

e Store heavy tools between thigh and shoulder height to avoid awkward lifting or twisting movements when removing or returning them.

f Tools that need oiling such as billhooks can be hung in racks with drip trays beneath that catch the oil. Use shallow trays half-filled with sand.

g Try to retain some space and flexibility within the storage system, so that if you acquire a few more tools it doesn't throw out the whole system.

h Although some dimensions are given in the following diagrams, most storage will need to be individually designed to fit the space available. Always check that tools are going to fit as you go along. If necessary build a 'mock-up' out of any rough timber before making decisions about materials and sizes. Check that you have left enough space for tools to be removed from racks, particularly where there are other racks or shelves above or below.

You should be able to make good use of second-hand timber, pallets and so on. Follow good carpentry practice, for example drill and screw rather than using nails, and with safety in mind, over-build rather than under-build.

The designs shown in this chapter are those which have been found to work well in various BTCV toolstores, but are not the only methods of storing such tools.

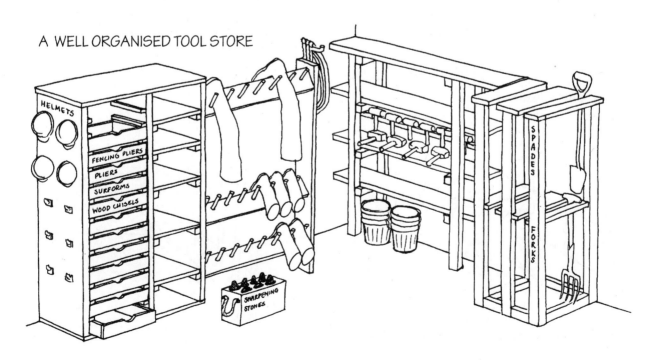

A WELL ORGANISED TOOL STORE

Axes

These can be stored heads down with the edges protected.

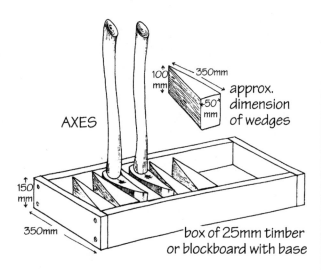

approx. dimension of wedges

AXES

box of 25mm timber or blockboard with base

Bowsaws

Always store bowsaws vertically, preferably with the tension on the blade released, to prolong blade life (p52). Good 'pegs' can be made out of sections of disused water pipe, especially those sections with an elbow. Use a large hammer drill (hire if necessary), to drill holes as deep as possible into the wall, and then hammer in pegs.

Hang spare bowsaw blades on a nail or peg. Spare blades can be safely transported into the field in a section of rigid plastic water pipe with a push-fit stopper.

hang bowsaw vertically with tension released

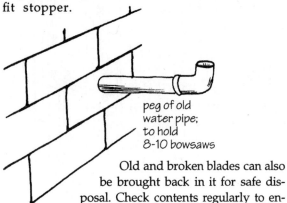

peg of old water pipe; to hold 8-10 bowsaws

Old and broken blades can also be brought back in it for safe disposal. Check contents regularly to ensure you have sufficient spares.

Crowbars & wrecking bars

Design the rack so that crowbars lean back towards the wall.

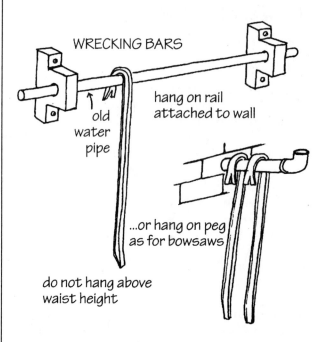

WRECKING BARS

old water pipe

hang on rail attached to wall

...or hang on peg as for bowsaws

do not hang above waist height

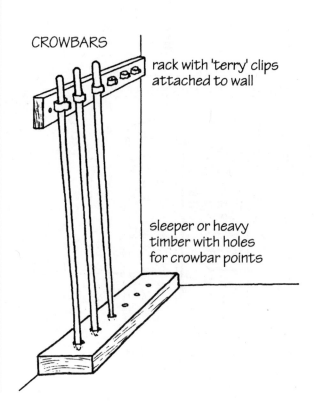

CROWBARS

rack with 'terry' clips attached to wall

sleeper or heavy timber with holes for crowbar points

22

'MANGER' RACKS FOR SPADES, SHOVELS + FORKS

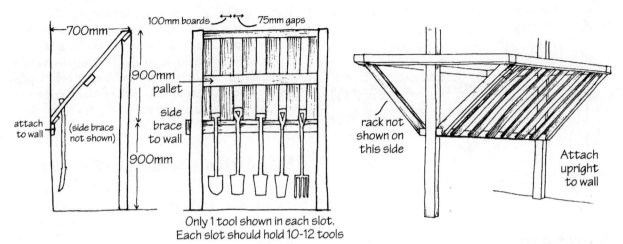

Only 1 tool shown in each slot.
Each slot should hold 10-12 tools

Spades, shovels and forks

Most groups will have quite a large number of these types of tools, and a good storage system is a basic requirement of the toolstore. 'Manger' type racks in which the tools can be hung work well, as they allow the tools to dry off and prevent any rust starting from being left in contact with the floor. Mangers can either be built freestanding, or against a wall, and can be made partly from pallets.

Horizontal racks can also be made in various ways to fit the available space.

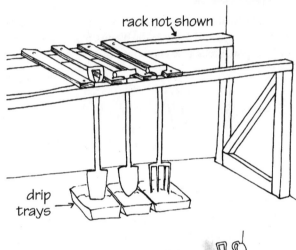

Rakes, hoes, pitchforks and cromes

These tools can be difficult to store, having long hafts, but no T or D handle with which to hang them. The rack shown has a wooden base to keep tools out of contact with the floor, to reduce the likelihood of rot or rust.

Another method of storage is to drill holes through the end of the tool handles, carefully smoothing the edges afterwards. A rack made from a plank of wood with 150mm (6") nails driven through can then be attached to the wall, and the tools hung from the nails.

Slashers can also be stored in this manner.

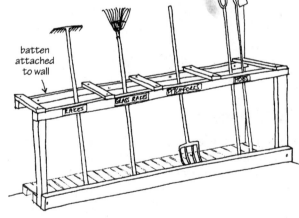

Mattocks and pickaxes

The hafts and heads are stored separately. The hafts can be stored in a rack, tea-chest or milk churn. The heads are best stored on old hafts, set upright as shown into a section of railway sleeper, or other heavy timber. Have at least one haft for each of the different types of heads, ie pickaxes, pick mattocks and grubbing mattocks.

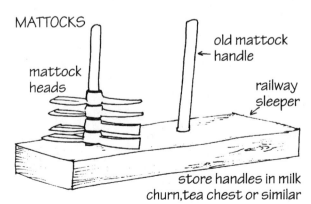

Sledgehammers and mells

Make sure there is sufficient clearance to allow tools to be lifted out easily.

SLEDGEHAMMERS + MELLS

Slashers

The box with plywood dividers holds the slashers safely upright and protects the blades. Slashers can also be hung on a rack (see above).

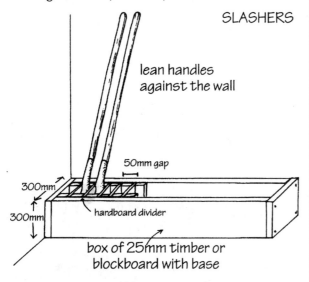

SLASHERS

lean handles against the wall

50mm gap

300mm

300mm

hardboard divider

box of 25mm timber or blockboard with base

Billhooks

After use, billhooks can be oiled and hung in this slatted rack, with drip trays underneath. Staffordshire, Southern Counties and Yorkshire billhooks, as well as grass-hooks, can be stored this way. Store each type separately within the rack. Note the plywood or hardboard cover at the front of the rack to prevent hands reaching underneath.

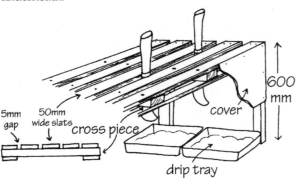

5mm gap

50mm wide slats

cross piece

cover

600 mm

drip tray

Winches

Winches should be stored in a dry position, off the floor. Winch cables are supplied on reels, on which they should also be stored. If a reel is not available, a winch cable can be stored inside an old car tyre, which is also a convenient way of transporting it, both in vehicles and on work sites. Before storing, put a little oil in the tyre, and then turn it to oil the cable. Always wear gloves when handling cables.

Miscellaneous large tools

These may include drive-alls and shuv-holers for fencing, rabbiting spades and other long or bulky items. Long-handled tools can be stored in a rack of the type shown for rakes and hoes. For safety, it is probably best to lay drive-alls on their sides. Don't put them in racks where you have to lean over a rail to lift them, as back injury is a likely result.

Miscellaneous small tools

These include hammers, fencing pliers, chisels, surforms, walling hammers and other tools mainly for fencing, carpentry and walling. These are best stored in hanging racks inside a cupboard. This gives some security, plus extra hanging space on the inside of the cupboard doors. Similar racks, not within a cupboard, can also be used. See opposite page for suggested cabinet.

Waders, wellies, gloves and helmets

Waders, wellies and gloves should be hung on racks in such a way that they can dry off after use, and so that they can be easily paired and counted. If possible, put the racks in the driest and/or draughtiest position in the toolstore, to reduce the chance of mould forming. Use fungicidal spray in wellies and waders to prevent the spread of foot diseases and promote hygiene.

Well-designed racks do take up a lot of space. Contain the problem by being ruthless about throwing out worn and leaky items, and only keep what you really need.

General purpose gloves are often of one size and type, so need not be kept in their original pairs, as long as a right and left can be quickly found. One idea is to hang all the 'rights' together on one rack, and all the 'lefts' together on another.

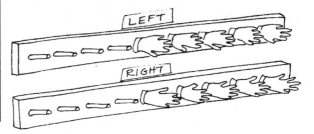

LEFT

RIGHT

SMALL TOOLS – CARPENTRY + FENCING

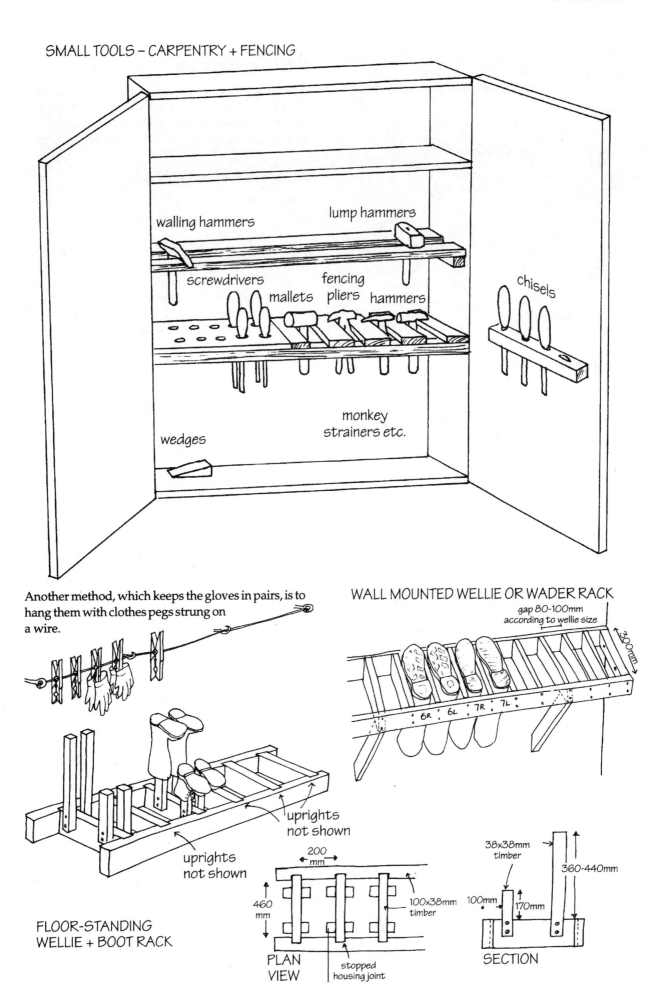

walling hammers

lump hammers

screwdrivers

mallets

fencing pliers

hammers

chisels

monkey strainers etc.

wedges

Another method, which keeps the gloves in pairs, is to hang them with clothes pegs strung on a wire.

WALL MOUNTED WELLIE OR WADER RACK

gap 80-100mm according to wellie size

300mm

6R   6L   7R   7L

uprights not shown

uprights not shown

FLOOR-STANDING WELLIE + BOOT RACK

PLAN VIEW

200 mm

460 mm

100x38mm timber

stopped housing joint

38x38mm timber

100mm

170mm

360-440mm

SECTION

25

Helmets should be hung on pegs of wooden dowel or similar. Position them out of direct sunlight, as this degrades the plastic. Check regularly for damage (p52).

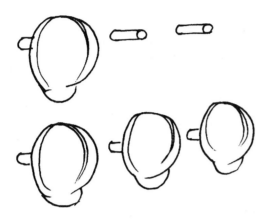

Ropes

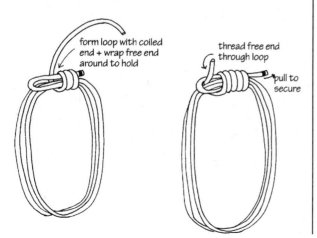

Ropes should always be coiled properly and hung up for storage. If the ropes are wet, coil them loosely until they are dry, and then coil them again and secure as shown below. When coiling rope, stand as shown and by turning the wrist, put a half twist into each coil. The half twist should go in the same direction as the coil of the rope, i.e. if you are coiling the rope in a clockwise direction, put a clockwise half twist in the rope. This makes the coils lie neatly, rather than twisting to form a figure of eight. Store ropes away from chemicals.

Fasten the coil as shown below:

form loop with coiled end + wrap free end around to hold

thread free end through loop

pull to secure

Stone boxes

Sharpening stones are fragile and can be easily broken, either by careless storage, transport or in the field. The best way to store and transport stones is in purpose-made boxes, well padded on the inside. (See opposite).

Project materials

Normally these are provided by the client, but some groups may have stores of various materials.

Joist hangers are a useful way of storing long pieces of timber. Space hangers at approximately one metre intervals. Store other long timbers on the floor on wooden chocks, to keep the timber out of contact with the floor. Avoid leaning long timbers against a wall, as this is dangerous, and can cause the timber to warp.

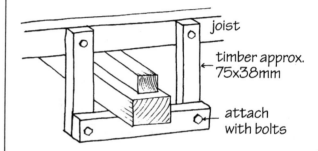

joist

timber approx. 75x38mm

attach with bolts

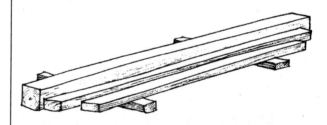

If possible, avoid storing any loose material such as sand or gravel. These are heavy, bulky and should be handled and transported the minimum amount neccessary. Cement deteriorates within a few weeks in storage, even unopened, so always buy fresh as you need it.

Broken tools

Put broken or damaged tools aside as soon as they are returned to the toolstore, so there is no chance of them being taken out again into the field. Provide a box for small tools, and a dustbin or tea chest for larger tools. See chapters 5 and 6 for details of tool repair.

BOX TO CONTAIN: 1 CANOE STONE; 1 AXE STONE + 1 CIGAR STONE

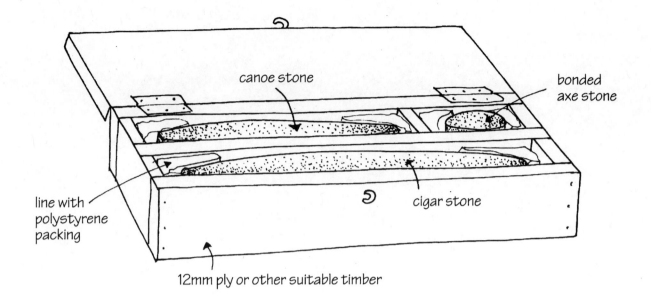

canoe stone

bonded axe stone

line with polystyrene packing

cigar stone

12mm ply or other suitable timber

4 Running the workshop and toolstore

Proper administration of your toolstore and workshop area, together with their associated activities, is essential. Without proper administration, damaged and missing tools will go unnoticed, volunteers will lose enthusiasm and projects will be difficult to run efficiently.

Your administration should take care of the following: records, security, tidiness, tool cleaning and maintenance, van loading and unloading and volunteer organisation. These topics are discussed further below.

Training in proper tool use in the field should also be a high priority, both for volunteer safety and to reduce damage to tools. Possibly the most common cause of tool breakage is incorrect use, or abuse, and prevention is better than cure. The six points which any user of a tool should know are:

1 The name of the tool.

2 The tool's general purpose.

3 The tool's specific use on the particular project.

4 How to carry the tool safely.

5 How to use it safely and correctly.

6 How to put it down safely.

For further information see the booklet *Hand Tools – a guide for safe use and care* (BTCV 1999) and BTCV *Leaders' Handbook.*

Records

These should include records of tools in and out, tools lost, tools under repair and purchase of new tools. Records are no problem as long as they kept up to date. Records are essential whether you have a few or many tools, as memory is not good enough, especially when it comes to handing on the administration to someone else. The information can be stored conventionally in files and log books, or on computer disc.

The following system is suggested:

a Keep copies of all correspondence. Never send a letter without keeping a copy, and ensure that it is dated and identifies both sender and recipient. Letters are best kept in a lever arch file in date order.

b Keep all delivery advice notes, bills, receipts etc, in a lever arch file in date order.

c Maintain a log recording losses (if noticed), breakages, deliveries, repairs, spare parts used, tool loans (if you allow them) and returns. One line per event with a date is sufficient. Keep a separate log for items which need specialist repair and maintenance. These may include winches, chainsaws, workshop power tools, fire extinguishers and gas bottles. Note any forward dates for regular service checks, plus dates when items which have a limited life, such as helmets, should be replaced (p53).

d Once a year do a stock take of everything in the toolstore and workshop. Compare the resulting list with the previous year's stock take, and taking into account the log, highlight any discrepancies. Make the lists as detailed as you can, for example if you have similar tools of different makes or designs, record the quantity of each type. Ideally each tool should be stamped with its own serial number (for details see below under 'Security'). Painted stock numbers wear off too quickly to be much use. Having compared your stock take with the previous year's, list your losses or gains, and take action as necessary to improve your administration.

Keep the files on a shelf in the workshop, together with instructional manuals and any other relevant literature.

A pinboard with paper and non-removable pen is useful for messages and reminders.

Security

This covers the security of your equipment both inside the toolstore and workshop and out in the field.

Keep a record of all key holders to the building. Keys kept on the premises should be signed in and out. Hang keys in a key cupboard where their absence will be noticed, and lock the key cupboard itself when the premises are unattended.

Tools should be marked in such a way that makes them easily visible in the field, and differentiates them from tools belonging to other groups you may work with. The usual method is to mark the handle with a band or bands of a bright colour gloss paint. Care must be taken to position the band in such a way that the paint does not cause injury to the hands of the user. This is especially important with long-handled tools, where the hand slides along the handle during use. Some people prefer not to paint the handle at all, but to paint a mark on the steel part of the tool.

Luminous blue and green paints are the most effective colours. Reds and oranges tend to merge with leaf litter in fading light. A neat band of colour shows up better than a rough splodge of paint, which tends to camouflage with the surroundings. Painted bands will need renewing at intervals as the paint wears off.

Tools can also be permanently stamped or branded with numbers, letters or other marks. Sets of number or letter punches can be used, so that you can mark a tool with its own individual code. This is useful for security, and when stock taking (see above). Punches can be used on pressed or forged steel (but not cast tools e.g. mell heads), wood or plastic. A full set of 10 numbers and 27 characters costs about £30.

Other methods are to use branding irons or marking stamps, made up to your requirements. These are useful for differentiating your group's tools from other people's, but does not give each tool its own individual code. Branding irons can be used on timber or plastic, and marking stamps on steel, timber or plastic.

Number and letter punches, branding irons or marking stamps should be available to order from good ironmongers, or through the classified advertisements of woodworking and other trade magazines.

Tidiness

Keeping the toolstore and workshop tidy is of the utmost importance. Failure to do so creates the problems of mislaid tools, lost tools going unnoticed, and making the place unsafe and inefficient to work in. Volunteers will be reluctant to work in an untidy workshop or spend time continually clearing up.

In setting up, you should have worked to the motto 'A place for everything and everything in its place'. By keeping to this as you go along you will, without too much effort, cut out the above problems and avoid the need for tedious and regular tidying up sessions.

It is useful to have a plan pinned near the door of the toolstore showing the location of the various tool racks, so that new volunteers can quickly see where things go. Make sure all racks and shelves are clearly labelled with what they are meant to contain.

General tool maintenance

Tools must always be cleaned before they are put away. Drying mud can accelerate rusting, and makes handles rough for the next user. Clean tools as far as possible in the field, whilst the mud is wet and easy to remove, and thus keep tool boxes and vehicles clean. At the toolstore, make cleaning easier by providing, if possible, an outside tap for washing muddy tools (p12), plenty of rags and oil, and drip trays beneath tool racks (p24). Saw

blades and spades are especially susceptible to rust if not cleaned and dried. All tool handles should also be wiped with an oily rag from time to time, using linseed oil. Alternatively, the tool can be immersed in a tank of linseed oil for a few days.

For general oiling buy ordinary vegetable oil. This becomes sticky with age, so purchase in the quantity which suits your needs. Old sump oil contains impurities which can cause damage and may be carcinogenic.

Like general tidiness, the system will work as long as everyone keeps to it. Once a few tools are put away uncleaned, other people will cease to bother. Check tools regularly for signs of damage, and repair as a preventative measure. This is better than waiting for tools to break in use.

Tools such as axes, mells and sledgehammers may get too dry if stored in a warm place, which can cause the hafts to shrink and the heads to become loose. Cure by immersing the tool in water for a few hours before use. It's best not to make a habit of this as constant wetting and drying can lead to weakness as a result of wood rot, as well as rusting the head.

Once your workshop is running you can introduce a programme of seasonal maintenance. For example, during the summer concentrate on the tools mainly not needed during that season, such as axes, billhooks and saws. Conversely, in the winter maintenance can be carried out on construction tools mainly used in the summer.

Van loading

All sharp-edged tools should be transported in such a way that the edges are protected. Strong hessian sacks are useful both for protecting and carrying sharp-edged tools. Hessian sacks are available from sack suppliers (see Yellow Pages or advertisements in farming magazines). Wrap and pack tools in the toolstore rather than by the van. Don't overload any sack with more than can be safely carried.

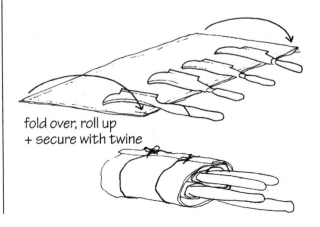

fold over, roll up
+ secure with twine

Bowsaws should always be transported with their plastic blade guards fitted. Put four or five 530mm (21") saws in a hessian sack and fold neatly to keep them together. For the larger bowsaws, put two or three in a sack. Spare saw blades can be carried in a section of plastic drainage pipe with push-fit ends (available from builders' merchants). Slashers should be placed two or three in a sack, and spades three or four in a sack. Mattock heads and handles should be transported separately, with the heads in a sack.

Billhooks can be wrapped in a doubled-over sack as shown, and then tied with string.

Small fencing and construction tools should be transported in tool boxes. Old metal ammunition boxes 840mm (33") long are ideal, but are now difficult to obtain. Similar capacity heavy-duty plastic tool storage boxes are available from DIY suppliers. Full tool boxes should be carried by two people.

When transporting tools, always ensure that passenger safety is not compromised. In crewbuses, transport tools in the boxes provided beneath the vehicle seats, or use a trailer. When loading, put all the heavy weight low down. Try to weight both sides equally. Put long-handled tools in first, with short-handled tools on top. All tools and gas bottles should be secured in case of accident. Roofracks should not be used for heavy tools, or stacked above 300mm (12") high. The maximum roofrack storage weight should never exceed 100kg.

The first aid kit should be the last item into the van and the first out, to ensure it is always accessible.

Tool lists should be kept on clipboards if they are to last the loading session. Tools should be counted out of the store by the person with the tool list. Another person should stay at the van to be responsible for the loading. An example of a tool list is given on the following pages. When making your own list, group similar items together and/or relate the order of the list to the storage plan of your toolstore.

Volunteer organisation

Safety considerations

Workshops and toolstores can be dangerous places, and careful consideration must be given to all aspects of safety. The management must ensure that all volunteers and employees are familiar with fire precautions (p19), safe storage of chemicals, petrol and gas (p18) and the proper storage of tools (chapter 3).

Nobody should undertake work in the workshop unless they have received proper training for the tools and equipment they are to use. Check that the insurance for your group covers workshop accidents.

A quarter of industrial accidents are caused while lifting and handling tools and materials, so particular attention must be paid to encouraging safe working practices. Safe storage of tools and equipment in accessible, well-laid out and properly lit premises is a good start.

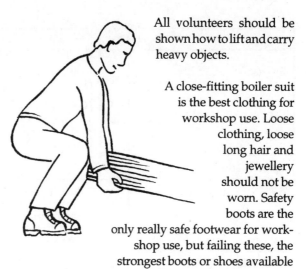

All volunteers should be shown how to lift and carry heavy objects.

A close-fitting boiler suit is the best clothing for workshop use. Loose clothing, loose long hair and jewellery should not be worn. Safety boots are the only really safe footwear for workshop use, but failing these, the strongest boots or shoes available should be worn. Safety goggles and ear defenders should be provided and used with equipment such as grinders.

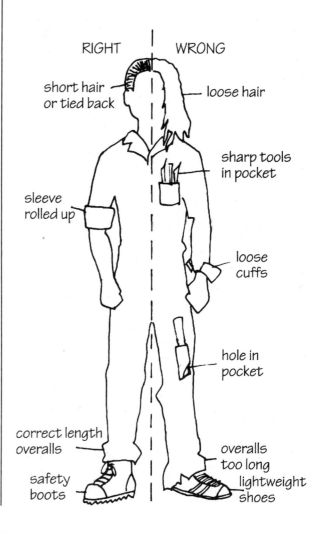

RIGHT   WRONG

short hair or tied back — loose hair

sharp tools in pocket

sleeve rolled up

loose cuffs

hole in pocket

correct length overalls — overalls too long lightweight shoes

safety boots

TOOLCARE

Project .... Date ....

Work .... Vehicle ....

Accommodation .... Number of volunteers ....

ITEM	needed	packed
Bow-saws 21"		
24"		
30"		
36"		
Spare blades		
Axes under 4lbs		
5lbs		
over 6lbs		
Billhooks Yorks		
Small		
Slasher curved		
heavy-duty		
Sickle		
Stone box		
Toggle loppers		
Chainsaw set		
Saw & tool kit		
Fuel & oil		
Helmet & visor		
Trousers		
Gloves		
Breaking bar		
Winch set		
Body		
Handle		
Cable		
Slings		
Ground anchor		
Extension cable		
Pulley blocks		
Crosscut saw		
Hand chain saw		
Reed/weed cutter		

ITEM	needed	packed
Spades Garden		
Trenching		
Hand trowel		
Shovel Large		
Small		
Post-hole auger		
Shuv-holer		
Forks Garden		
Hand		
Pitch		
Rakes		
Cromes		
Mattocks Pick		
Grubbing		
Pickaxe		
Crowbar		
Wrecking bar		
Drivall (Post driver)		
Mell		
Beetle		
Sledgehammer		
Tamper		
Wheelbarrow		
Plank		
Bucket		
Rope		
Grapple		
Dibber		
First Aid kit		
Water container	1 full	
Spare container		
Sales bag		
Sign board		

ITEM	needed	packed
Collecting box		
Book box		
Calor bottles		
One-ring burner		
1 double burner		
2 double burners		
Large burner		
Calor boiler		
Tea-box & Kettle	1 day	
Food & Kettle	1 res	
Vegetable box	1 res	
Cutlery box	1 res	
Domestic box	1 res	
Bowl	1 res	
Karrimats		
Camp beds		
Blankets		
Wellies		
Waders		
Safety helmets		
Gloves		
Hammers Claw		
Club		
Brace & bits		
Carpenters Ripsaw		
Hacksaw		
Surform		
Wood chisel		
Cold chisel		
Pliers Fencing		
Other		
Mole wrench		
Wire cutters		

ITEM	needed	packed	ITEM		needed	packed	ITEM		needed	packed
Bolt cutters			Nails	Small			Sump oil & rags			
Wire strainers				Large			Primus set			
Mallet			String balls				Paraffin			
Spirit level			Amcide	Pot			Lighting box			
Tape measure				Brush			Toilet	Elsan toilet		
Boxwood ruler				Goggles				Elsan chemicals		
Square				Gloves				Toilet tent		
Steel wedges			Creosote	Pot			14' Ridge tent			
Fence wire				Brush			Stormhaven tent			
Tying wire				Goggles			Tent repair kit			
Staples				Gloves						

FURTHER INSTRUCTIONS AND EXTRA EQUIPMENT

33

Training

Within your group you may have sufficient expertise and experience to run your own 'in house' training sessions on workshop skills, though the value of external training courses even for those who think they are skilled should not be forgotten.

BTCV organises training courses on workshop skills. Contact BTCV headquarters or nearest office for details. Training workshop skills may also be available through Lantra Connect (Tel: 0345 078007 www.lantra.co.uk). Local agricultural colleges and local authority adult education services are also worth contacting. Even if they do not have suitable courses, they may be able to put you in touch with someone who will be able to run a course or session specifically for your group.

Provided you have a skilled trainer and suitable workshop facilities, you can do most of your own training 'in house'. Put your efforts into organising a series of sessions over a period of a few weeks, rather than hoping people will turn up over a prolonged period for indeterminate sessions of 'training', tidying up and other odd jobs. Try organising a series of perhaps four or five evening sessions in the early autumn or during the post new year lull.

Make sure you match the number of trainees with the bench space and tools which you have available, and ensure you have sufficient supply of all spares and other equipment necessary. Arrange for a deputy to take over in case the trainer is unable to take a session.

Structure the course so that trainees know what topics are going to be covered, and try to introduce a new skill at each session. Make the sessions as sociable and enjoyable as possible, and provide tea and biscuits or a visit to the pub afterwards.

From the group of trainees, hopefully a small band of enthusiasts will evolve who will use their skills to maintain the tools and generally run the workshop and toolstore. Try to keep to a regular weekly or fortnightly session. Agree on the various responsibilities for organisation, such as key holding, ordering of spares, tea supplies etc. If someone has a particular interest in one aspect of tool maintenance, and no one else objects, let them get on with it, though encourage them to train a deputy! Otherwise, try and make sure that everyone has a turn at the various jobs that need doing. Keep the evenings sociable, and run a course of training sessions at least once a year so that newcomers aren't excluded.

5   Replacing hafts and handles

The advice given below assumes some knowledge of how to use carpentry and metalworking tools, such as Surforms, files, hacksaws, drills and so on. People not familiar with these tools should refer to a general DIY manual. In some cases there may be more than one means of achieving the desired result, but for brevity only one alternative is usually given.

Tools and materials

Tools

You should have, and know how to use, the tools listed on page 15 for rehafting.

Some people find it worthwhile making up special wooden jigs to hold particular tools in the vice, although others prefer to hold the tool directly in the vice. If doing the latter, then use timber padding or plastic inserts to prevent damage to the haft.

Some examples of jigs are shown on this page.

Hafts and handles

Hafts can either be ash, which is the traditional English wood, or hickory, which is an American import. Hickory

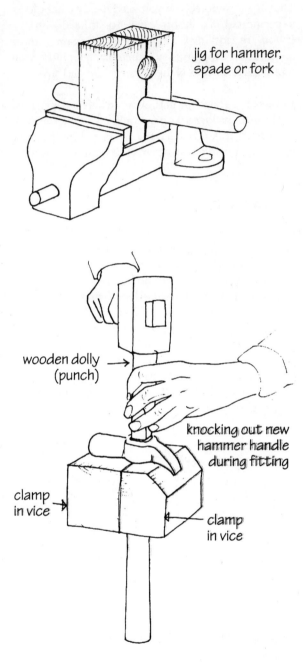

jig for hammer, spade or fork

wooden dolly (punch)

knocking out new hammer handle during fitting

clamp in vice

clamp in vice

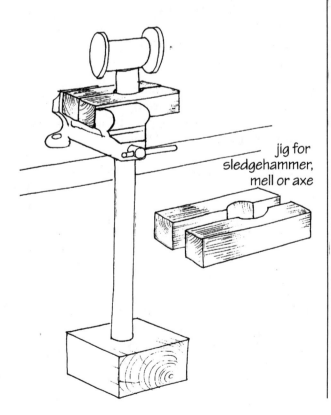

jig for sledgehammer, mell or axe

is stronger and less elastic than ash, but it is also more expensive. Heavy striking tools such as mells, sledgehammers and axes should always be rehafted with hickory. Hickory is also recommended for slashers. Picks, mattocks and claw hammers, which have to withstand striking and levering actions, should also have hickory hafts. Ash is best used only on light hammers or those with short hafts such as lump hammers, and on spades, shovels, forks, rakes and hoes.

Choose handles that are knot-free, and without bruises or splits. Bare wood, which will absorb linseed oil, is better than varnished wood. If buying hafts with pre-sawn wedge slots, check that these are centrally cut.

The size of the sockets in otherwise similar tool heads can vary considerably. If you need to buy a handle for a specific tool, take the broken tool or its head with you. If you are stocking a large workshop against future needs, order a range of sizes, unless you know all your tool stock has heads of the same weight and size.

In matching a head to a haft, choose a haft that is slightly oversize in thickness (you are unlikely to find one that is an exact fit!). Considerably oversized hafts can be used, but shaving them down to fit requires a lot more work.

Cutting wedges

Cutting a wedge is not easy, and is best done with a tenon saw. Use hardwood, such as oak, aligned so that the grain runs the same way as the haft. The sides of the wedge should be flat, with no bumps or hollows. The wedge should have the same length and depth as the length and depth of the slot in the haft. The width at the fat end depends on the degree of taper of the tool socket. You will almost certainly need to make the wedge thicker than you think. As a rough guide try 5mm for mells, 10mm for sledgehammers and 15mm for axes. The thin end should be the same width as the slot, or very slightly fatter.

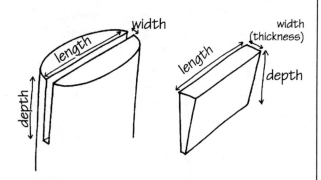

General approach to the job

Most rehafting work involves the following basic stages:

1 Remove the stump of the old handle. This may take time and trouble, but never resort to burning out the old handle as this can ruin the tool head (see below).

2 Match the head to the replacement handle, making sure the head is the right way round. If the hole of the head is slightly tapered, the wider end should be away from the user.

3 Carefully shave off the wood from the handle until it fits tightly and to the correct depth into the tool head. While doing this, test for fit frequently, as wood that has been shaved off cannot be put back! A Surform with a sharp blade is the easiest tool to use, but a rasp, spokeshave, draw knife or, occasionally, mallet and chisel can be used. Give a final smoothing with sandpaper.

4 Fit the head and secure it to the haft.

5 Check that the handle is smooth. Brand or paint identification mark if required, then oil with linseed oil.

Some common errors!

a The haft is not a good fit in the socket. The most frequent error is to take too much off the extreme end producing a pencil-end effect. (This does not apply to blind-socketed and strapped tools such as slashers.)

b The haft is shaped to fit the socket, but is left with a sharp change in thickness where it leaves the head. This concentrates the stress at one point, so the haft may break in use.

c The head is fitted back to front. This is generally obvious on axes, but is not so obvious on other tools such as sledgehammers.

d The head is fitted upside down.

e The wooden wedge is too fat, so that it cannot be driven in fully, or less commonly, is too thin, resulting in a loose head. This applies to axes, mells and sledgehammers.

f The handle stump is burnt out by placing the broken tool head in a bonfire. This can get rid of the old haft, but may damage the temper (springiness) of the metal, which ruins the tool head.

g The handle is bruised by overtightening in a metal-jawed vice.

h Cast iron heads are cracked by being struck hard with a hammer, or over tightened in a metal-jawed vice.

i The head is fitted at an angle due to uneven shaving off of surplus wood from the handle.

j The replacement haft is too long. Ready-tapered hafts for spades and other tools are often supplied too long, and the temptation is to fit them as they are, rather than cut a new taper.

Removing stumps of broken handles

This can require a substantial amount of work, so make sure you choose the best approach to the problem.

There are four main types of head/haft interface:

a Blind- or open-socketed, e.g. slashers, Yorkshire bill-hooks, some spades.

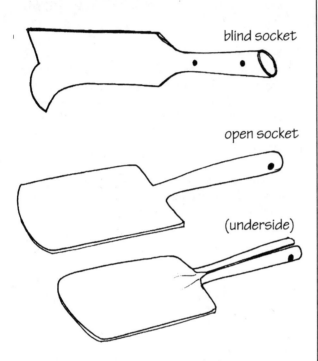

blind socket

open socket

(underside)

b Strapped, e.g. some pitchforks and spades.

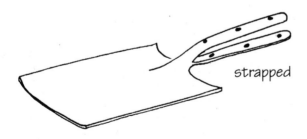

strapped

c Solid head with tapered socket, e.g. axes and some sledgehammers

tapered socket

handle to this side

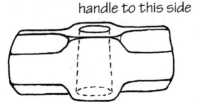

d Solid head with parallel-sided socket, e.g. mell.

parallel socket

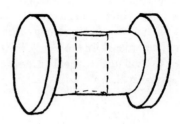

Note that not all similar tools are constructed alike. For example, some manufacturer's cromes are strapped, whereas others are blind-socketed.

For situations like (a) and (b) first remove the rivets. The usual method for this is to centre punch the rivet head, then using the mark as a guide, drill down into the rivet. Use a sharp drill bit slightly smaller than the rivet (you may have to guess at this until the first rivet is removed).

Work from one side only. Take care not to enlarge the rivet hole in the tool head itself. Then use a blunt-ended punch struck with a hammer to punch out the rest of the rivet. The head can then be removed by pulling it off, if

there is enough left of the old handle to get a grip on. If the old handle has broken off inside the socket you will have to remove it by drilling out piecemeal.

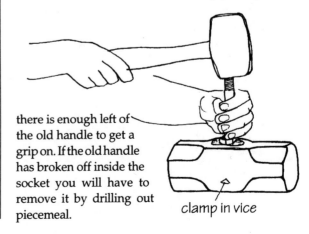

clamp in vice

For situations like (c) and (d), cut off the old handle flush with the tool head. Apply a large flat ended punch (a bolt with a flat head is suitable), and hammer this to knock out the handle stump, see above. This is not always easy, and you may need to drill a series of holes to free the old handle. Note that for case (c) you should punch from the side where the handle has been cut off, otherwise you will just wedge the stump more firmly into the tapered socket.

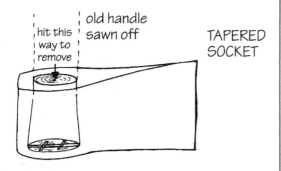

An alternative method which is usually successful with most tools is to saw off the broken handle flush with the end of the socket, then drill a hole and screw in a coach screw. Hold the screw head in a vice, and knock the spade with a mallet or club hammer to remove the stump.

Socketed tools

1 Remove the old haft. If the stump comes out in one piece use it as a visual guide to the shaping of the new haft.

2 Check the socket of the tool head for dents, and also the edges of the rivet holes which are frequently bent inwards. These should be hammered out whilst

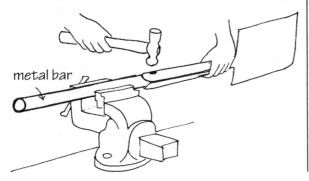

supporting the tool socket from the inside with a solid round section bar held in a vice.

3 Select a haft of the correct length by matching it with the old haft or with a new or correctly repaired tool of the same type. Ready-tapered spade and other hafts are often supplied too long, and a new taper will have to be made. If the length is suitable, check whether the taper fits the socket. The haft must be oversize at the 'fat' end of the socket, or an exact fit. Don't try to save work by selecting a smaller haft that will fit loosely at this end of the socket, as it will soon snap.

4 Clamp the haft in a vice, using a jig as necessary (p35) and carefully shave off excess wood. Rotate frequently and check for fit. The haft must penetrate to the far end of the socket. This can be checked by measuring the depth of the socket, marking this measurement on the haft and then making sure the haft penetrates as far as this mark.

5 Hafts of spades and forks require special care, as the sockets are often tapered, and you must check that the D or T grip handle is parallel with the blade of the tool.

6 When you are quite certain that the fit is correct, apply linseed oil to the part of the haft which is to be fitted into the socket. Don't oil the whole haft yet, or it will be slippery and difficult to handle. Then proceed to riveting. Select a rivet of the right diameter for the pre-drilled holes in the socket. Checking the alignment of the blade to the handle, fit the head to the shaft and knock it home with a woodworking mallet.

Clamp the tool head in the vice, and drill accurately through the rivet holes into the haft, using a drill the same thickness as the rivet. Take great care to line up the drill with the holes; if in doubt drill halfway through, reverse the tool head and drill the rest of the way from the other side, so that the two holes meet in the centre of the shaft. This method also avoids splitting the wood at the exit point of the drill hole.

Some people prefer to scribe round the inside of the rivet holes with a pencil, and then remove the haft from the head before drilling. This is because the flutes of the drill otherwise tend to catch on the metal. In this case, apply linseed oil to the haft head after drilling.

7 Fit the rivet. Cut off surplus with a hacksaw, leaving about 3mm protruding. If the rivet is not a tight fit in the tool head, leave rather more rivet protruding. Remove tool head from vice.

8 Support the head of the rivet against an anvil or other solid metal block. Then using a ball pein hammer, form the end of the rivet by carefully hammering to mushroom it out. Take your time, as many gentle blows form a neater head than a few very forceful ones. Rough rivets make a tool uncomfortable to use.

Common errors are:

a Rivet is not tight. More hammering needed.

b Lopsided rivet head. To prevent this, work carefully all around the rivet head.

c Rivet head is too big. This is due to too much metal being left after the end of the rivet was cut off.

d Check the finished rivet for smoothness at both ends and file if necessary, but beware of filing into the metal of the tool head.

e Check the smoothness of the haft and use sandpaper if necessary to rub down. Mark or paint if desired. Treat with linseed oil and leave to dry.

Strapped tools

Proceed as for socketed tools, but take account of the following points:

a Broken hafts can be removed from the straps by cutting down the centre of the haft. However this does destroy the shaped end of the haft which cannot then be used as a model for the new haft. Where possible, use the drilling method described above. If you do decide to saw down the haft, use a hacksaw when nearing the position of the rivets. Once the rivets are severed they can generally be worked loose and levered out from one side, and then the remaining half can be punched out.

b After removing the old haft, check that the straps are still strong enough to make rehafting worthwhile, as they are of relatively thin metal and tend to rust away faster than the rest of the tool head.

c Most strapped spades, forks and shovels have hafts with curved points. When shaping, clamp them in the vice with the point towards the floor, rather than rotating them as described for socketed tools.

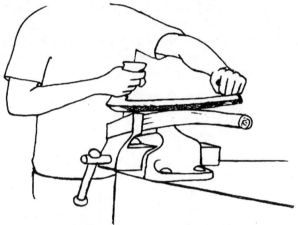

The straps have some flexibility, but the new haft must be shaved down to the same dimensions as the old one. Don't force an oversized haft into place.

d Once the haft fits correctly between the straps of the tool head, clamp the tool in the vice. The middle hole should be drilled and riveted first, then reposition the tool in the vice and drill out the hole nearest the tool head. Before drilling the final hole (furthest from the blade), it may be necessary to temporarily bind the top of the neck tightly with cord to bring them into contact with the new haft. Remove cord after fitting the rivet.

e To finish off, hammer the exposed edge of the neck to remove the sharp rough edge. Rotate the haft and 'dress' the remaining three edges in the same way.

Tanged tools

On a tanged tool, the end of the tool head is forged into a point, which is inserted into a hole in the haft of the

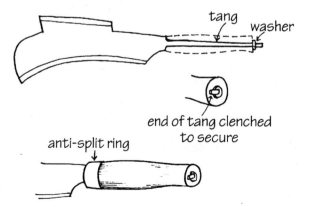

handle. A through tang goes through the length of the handle and protrudes at the end, where it is clenched to secure. Billhooks and grasshooks have this type of tang.

Tools such as chisels and files, with which there is no danger of the head flying off in proper use, have short tangs. The handles should be checked regularly for any faults, such as chips and splinters. Replacement handles on most files will need to be 'step-drilled' in order to get a good fit. Clamp the handle in a vice and drill as shown, then remove from the vice. Clamp the file in the vice and then tap the new handle on with a wooden mallet. Almost all of the tang should be inside the handle, as the tang of a file is of soft metal, which if not fitted properly inside the handle, will bend in use.

STEP-DRILLING A FILE HANDLE

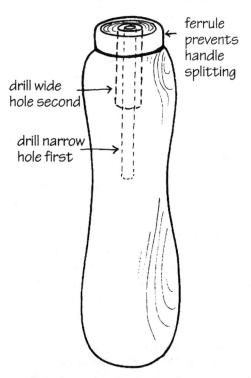

ferrule prevents handle splitting

drill wide hole second

drill narrow hole first

Damaged plastic handles have to be cut off using a junior hacksaw, taking care not to damage the tang. Replace with a wooden handle.

Through tanged tools

Handles that are slightly loose can sometimes be tightened by hammering the clenched end of the tang. If this does not work, a replacement handle may be needed.

The hole drilled through the new handle will need to be enlarged at the end nearest the tool blade, using a large diameter drill.

The tang must protrude sufficiently from the end of the handle for a washer to be fitted, and the end of the tang clenched over. If necessary shorten the handle by cutting a slice off the end.

Make sure the replacement handle has its anti-split ring fitted before hammering it into position.

Mells and sledgehammers

A mell has a cast-iron head. The head must not be hit with a metal hammer, or clamped tightly in a metal-jawed vice, as it may crack. Mells have parallel-sided sockets.

A sledgehammer has a forged steel head, and slightly tapered socket.

The procedure for rehafting is as follows:

1 Remove the old handle. Clamp the head in a vice, protecting it in a wooden jig or padding (p35). Drill three or four holes around the outside of the haft head, taking care to avoid the metal wedges. Then knock out the remains of the old haft, using a hammer and punch or blunt chisel. Retrieve the metal wedges if possible.

2 Select a new haft and test it for fit. Clamp the haft in the vice and carefully using a surform, shape to fit. The haft should remain parallel-sided, both for mells and sledgehammers, and great care must be taken to avoid producing a pencil-point effect or an angled head to the haft. Rotate the haft in the vice to produce a parallel finish. See also page 41.

3 If the haft is supplied without a slot for the wedge, you will need to saw one. Clamp the haft vertically in

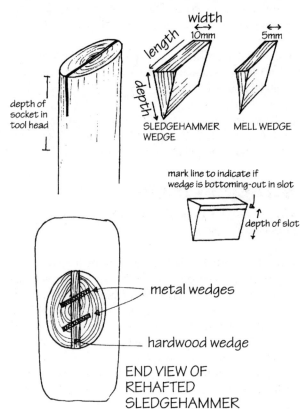

depth of socket in tool head

width 10mm

length

depth

SLEDGEHAMMER WEDGE

5mm

MELL WEDGE

mark line to indicate if wedge is bottoming-out in slot

depth of slot

metal wedges

hardwood wedge

END VIEW OF REHAFTED SLEDGEHAMMER

the vice, and using a tenon saw, cut a slot about half the depth of the socket. Select or cut (p36) a hardwood wedge to fit the slot. The length of the wedge should match the slot, with the depth slightly greater than the depth of the slot. The width can only be judged by experience of rehafting, but the following gives a guide. On a mell, having a parallel-sided socket, the haft will already be a close fit. The wedge can therefore be slim, with a thickness of no more than 5mm at the fat end. For the tapered socket of a sledgehammer, the wedge is needed to force the haft ends outwards and therefore the wedge needs to be about 10mm thick.

To drive the shaft into the head, hold the end of the handle with one hand banging down near the ground. Use a mallet to hit the end of the handle, driving the haft into the head. Take care not to 'ground' the head when doing this.

4 Before fitting the wedge, dip it in linseed oil. This makes it easier to fit, and takes oil into the heart of the shaft. To fit the wedge, position the tool head correctly on the haft, and with the tool held vertically and the haft end on a solid floor or wooden block, drive the wedge home. Use a hard wooden mallet, or, if using a steel hammer, protect the top of the wedge with a wooden billet. After hitting the wedge home, there should be no more than 1 or 2mm excess protruding. Cut this off flush using a hacksaw.

5 Select one or two metal wedges. These need to fit diagonally across the wedged end of the haft without touching the metal of the tool head. Drive these home using a hammer. Finish by using a punch to drive them just below the surface of the wood.

6 Check that the handle is smooth, paint marking band as required, and oil with linseed oil. Oiling can be done by immersing the whole head in oil for a few days.

Hammers

For the purpose of rehafting, hammers can be divided into two groups. The claw or carpenter's hammer usually has a tapered socket and long neck, and is quite simple to rehaft. The wedge is set diagonally. Pin, cross pein, ball pein and brick hammers have a short tapered socket and are more difficult to rehaft, as the shortness of the socket makes it harder to get the handle really tight. The wedge is normally set in line with the hammer head.

Before rehafting, file off any burrs from the inside of the eye or on the outer surface of the hammer head. Ball pein and claw hammers in particular may need to have their working surfaces dressed, first by filing if very pitted, and then finishing off with wet and dry paper.

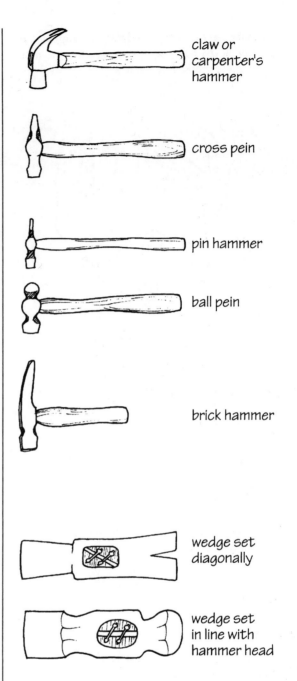

claw or carpenter's hammer

cross pein

pin hammer

ball pein

brick hammer

wedge set diagonally

wedge set in line with hammer head

The basic procedure for rehafting is as for sledgehammers, but note the following:

1 Sometimes it may be possible to re-use an old haft, by sawing off the damaged end. Check that the remaining tapered section up to the shoulder is long enough to reach through the socket or 'eye'. If it isn't, discard it and use a new haft.

2 Using a surform, carefully shape the taper to fit the hammer eye. Check progress frequently by holding the end of the haft against the eye of the hammer. When the haft fits far enough into the head for it to stay on without being held in place, carry out a test fit. This is done by holding the hammer clear of the bench, as shown, and hitting the end of the haft a few times with a wooden mallet until the haft has been driven into the head as far as it will go. If the tapered

end of the haft has not reached right through the eye, then knock the head off and remove a little more wood where marked by the head.

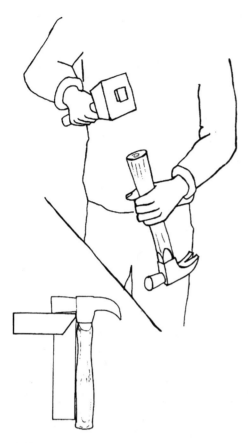

3 The head of the hammer should be at right angles to the haft, as shown.

4 The slot for the wedge should be about one third the depth of the eye.

Axes

Head shapes and socket dimensions in axes are very variable. Make sure you select the correct haft for the tool you are repairing.

Note the following:

1 When shaping the haft to fit the socket, make sure you have the head the correct way round. This is not always obvious as some axes, such as Canadian axes have nearly symmetrical blades.

2 Take your time with shaping and fitting. Axes take a lot of stress in normal use, and a well-fitted haft is essential. A correctly fitted head should rest on a flat surface as shown below.

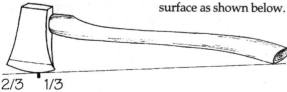

2/3   1/3

3 The general procedure is as for sledgehammers and mells (p41). A large wedge will be needed, with a thickness of 10-15mm.

Punners

On most punners, the haft is fixed to the head by a rivet. This is usually the point at which the haft breaks. A stronger repair can be made by using a blind or fox wedge.

Shave the haft until it fits tightly in the socket of the head, and then make a saw cut in the end to about half the depth of the socket. Make a hardwood wedge of the same depth and a little over twice as thick as the saw cut, and to fit the full width of the haft. Coat the wedge and the end of the haft with raw linseed oil, and then insert the wedge far enough to hold it. Then using a wooden mallet, drive the haft into the socket to secure. The bottom of the socket forces the wedge into the haft, giving a tight friction fit.

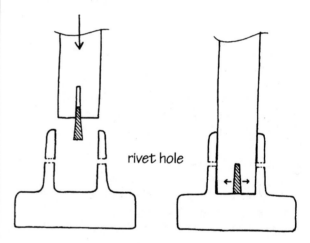

rivet hole

If you find that punner hafts are frequently being broken, it may be better to replace the wooden haft with a thick walled steel tube, drilled and fixed with a rivet. Some punner heads do not have a rivet hole, and can only be repaired using a blind wedge as described above.

6   Sharpening

This chapter covers the sharpening of slashers, billhooks, grasshooks, axes, spades, shovels, hoes, mattocks, picks, crowbars, chisels, secateurs, loppers and shears.

Saw sharpening is described in chapter 7.

General information

Sharpening edged tools involves two processes: grinding and honing. Grinding is done in the workshop with a machine sandstone, bench grinder or file. Honing is done with a stone, of which various types are available (see p15). Honing of most tools is done in the workshop, but tools used for cutting herbaceous growth, such as scythes and grasshooks, need honing in the field.

Cutting edges

The sketches opposite show various cutting edges in cross-section. An obtuse edge is often assumed to be blunt, and a fine edge to be sharp. In fact an obtuse edge can, and should be sharp, and a fine edge can, and should not, be blunt. (Note that 'obtuse' should not be taken in the strict geometrical sense, but merely as a contrast with 'acute'.) Of the examples sketched, only bluntness is always undesirable.

An acute edge will cut soft material, such as grass and other herbaceous growth, extremely well. It is particularly effective when drawn across the material like a knife, as when scything. However, it is a very fragile edge. If used percussively, like an axe, it is liable to fold over or crumple. It also drives deep without splitting the material, and is thus easily wedged in a wooden stem.

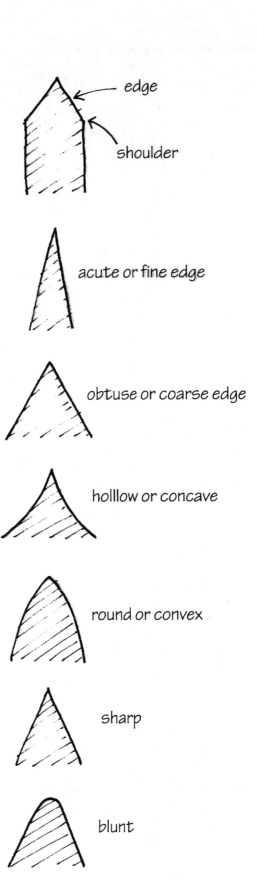

edge

shoulder

acute or fine edge

obtuse or coarse edge

holllow or concave

round or convex

sharp

blunt

An obtuse edge is not particularly effective with a knife action, though it will still cut a finger open, but it is very suitable for axes and some types of billhook. It is a durable edge, with the mass of material behind it lending strength at the moment of impact. An obtuse edge often runs onto convex cheeks, so that wood is forced apart vigorously without keeping a large area of metal pressing onto the wood cleft, and so binding.

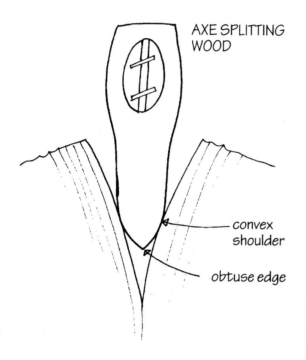

AXE SPLITTING WOOD

— convex shoulder

— obtuse edge

A hollow-cheeked or concave blade has in exaggeration many of the properties of a fine edge. It usually arises as a side effect of dressing with a grinding wheel, and is not often seen in conservation tools.

SHARPENING A FINE EDGE

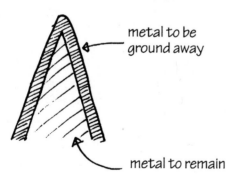

metal to be ground away

metal to remain

LAZY SHARPENING

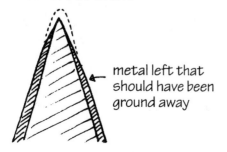

metal left that should have been ground away

Convex cheeks may arise unintentionally as a result of lazy sharpening. A lot of metal has to be removed to sharpen a blunt fine edge. The temptation is to improve the edge but with less grinding by making a more obtuse edge.

This is not always a bad idea. A reasonable strategy is to be slightly lazy on most occasions, doing enough to keep the edge sharp, and then removing the developing shoulder occasionally with a grinding wheel or coarse file. The important thing is not to let it get out of hand, particularly if no grinding wheel is available.

Equally importantly, avoid over enthusiastic acute grinding on edges which are supposed to be obtuse and/or convex-cheeked.

New tools are often supplied without proper edges. This is deliberate, as sharp edges are both dangerous and liable to damage in transit. It is for such tools that a grinding wheel is most needed, and it may be worth hiring one as necessary if many new tools need dressing. Thereafter, hand-held stones are quite adequate for normal sharpening, if proper care is taken when the tools are in use.

Responsibility for sharpening

You should have a definite policy about who is to sharpen tools. It is tempting to regard sharpening as a lot of hard work, and enlist as many helpers as you can to get the job done. However, proper sharpening requires time, skill and good workshop facilities. Incorrect sharpening by an untrained person can wreck an edge in a few moments, and restoration can take hours of hard work.

Ideally, after a day's work in the field, one or two trained people should give the tools a quick 'brush-up' sharpening before storing, putting aside any which need further sharpening or grinding. Once slightly blunt, tools get blunter much more quickly, and sharpening becomes a difficult and time consuming job. Then in addition train a few enthusiastic volunteers to make an effective team, who can organise special sessions to undertake tool sharpening and other repairs.

Sharpening procedure
Safety considerations

There are at least two schools of thought on the safest and most effective method of sharpening.

Some people maintain that the best results are achieved by running the file or stone towards the edge, and that this minimises the creation of burrs. If sharpening is done this way, the hand holding the file or stone MUST wear a protective leather glove, as the risk of cutting one's hand is high.

Other people maintain that there is no advantage in sharpening towards the edge, and that it is safer and just as effective to only sharpen with the file or stone running away from the edge. In this case it is not so essential that a glove be worn on the hand holding the stone, although accidents can still happen. With practice, it is also possible to learn to use the stone in either hand, in which case the tool can always be held with the blade facing away from the body.

It is recommended here that beginners should learn to sharpen by running the file or stone AWAY from the edge, and that a glove should be worn on the hand steadying the file end, or holding the stone. If possible, clamp the tool in a vice, so that either or both hands can be used on the stone or file. Never use a file without a handle, or there is a risk of the tang causing injury to the wrist and forearm.

A file cuts on the forward stroke only, and should be lifted off on the return stroke. Rubbing it back and forth will cause it to become blunt much more quickly.

A leather glove is cumbersome and stiff, and it makes your hands clumsy and grip weak, but you must put up with all that. Eventually you will overcome this and hardly notice it. Ideally, each person should have their own sharpening glove or gloves, which then harden to the shape of the hand. Don't use the same gloves for general use. Your sharpening gloves will get oily, and thus slippery and unsafe for field use.

Always wear goggles and gloves when using machine sandstones, bench grinders or angle grinders. These machines must only be used by operators who have received general training in their safe use, and specific training in their use for tool grinding and sharpening. Particular care must be taken when using angle grinders, which are hand-held, and with which there is less margin for error than with a bench-mounted machine.

Tool use

You should have, and know how to use, the tools listed on page 14 for sharpening.

A 260mm (10") mill file with one rounded edge is the best tool for filing off metal in quantity, and gives greater control and is quicker to use than a coarse stone. Finish the edge with a fine stone.

Make sure the stone is clean and free from grit before you use it, or you will damage the edge of the tool. Lubricate with vegetable oil or water. Don't use old engine oil as this contains harmful detergents and impurities such as bits of metal which can damage the stone or tool. As you work, wipe away any surplus oil off the stone and blade with a rag. As the blade becomes sharper it will 'bite' into the stone, and the feel and

sound of the blade on the stone will change.

If a sharpening stone becomes concave with use, it can be rubbed on a sheet of glass lubricated with oil and fine sand or grinding compound until it is flat. Use a small disused window in a sound frame, with the glass supported from beneath by a piece of wood or board, to avoid accidents. Fine sand and oil only work on natural stones such as Turkey, Washita or Arkansas. Artificial stones such as silicon carbide (carborundum) need a mixture of oil and silicon carbide powder or valve grinding paste.

Whatever you use, rubbing a stone flat is a daunting task, and it may be more cost effective to buy a new one.

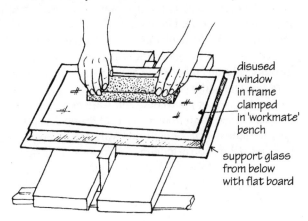

disused window in frame clamped in 'workmate' bench

support glass from below with flat board

It is well worth making up special jigs for holding tools during sharpening. The jig is clamped in the vice, holding the tool firmly and safely, and leaving both hands free for sharpening.

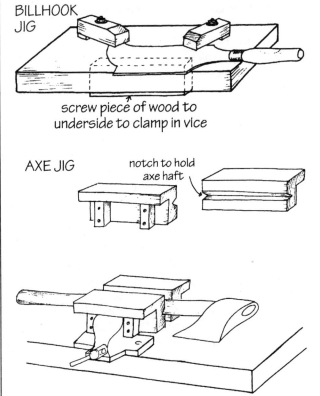

BILLHOOK JIG

screw piece of wood to underside to clamp in vice

AXE JIG

notch to hold axe haft

It is usually best to stand at the work bench, with legs apart and body over the work. The shoulders and upper body provide the pressure, while the arms and hands provide motion and accuracy.

Machines must only be used by trained operators. It is very easy to damage the edge of a tool by careless grinding, or to ruin the temper of a tool by letting it overheat. If the cutting edge turns blue, it has lost temper and will be impossible to sharpen. If this happens, you must grind off the blued areas and start again. Machine sandstones, bench grinders and angle grinders are described on page 14. The choice of which machine is used will depend on availability, the type of tool and amount of grinding to be done, and the preference and experience of the operator. Some operators prefer to use a bench-mounted machine, whereas others may like the flexibility of a hand-held machine. In skilled hands, an angle grinder is effective for most grinding jobs on billhooks, axes, mattocks, picks, crowbars, bolsters and cold chisels. Use a fairly coarse abrasive pad in new or good condition. Care must be taken to keep at least 2mm from the edge of the blade, and to keep the abrasive pad moving along the whole length to be dressed. Lift it off at the end of every length to inspect progress and allow the blade to cool down. Finish off with a file and sharpening stone when the worst has been dealt with.

Billhooks and slashers

Normally you should grind the blade at the same angle as it was set. Usually the edge has merely become blunt, and you can take the angle from the face immediately behind the edge, called the sharpening bevel. You are grinding quite a large area, so it may take longer than you expect. Resist the temptation to grind only the extreme edge, which will make the edge progressively more obtuse, and develop a shoulder where it is not wanted.

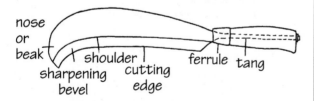

After grinding as necessary, sharpen with a coarse file and then hone with a fine canoe stone. Sharpen with diagonal strokes of the file or stone, stroking away from the edge, and lifting it on the return stroke. The strokes should be such that the file or stone slides both across and along the edge, so that nicks in the edge are ironed out rather than perpetuated. This action also minimises scoring of the stone. Work with several strokes from one end of the blade to the other, and then back on the opposite diagonal motion. Then turn the blade over and repeat on the other side.

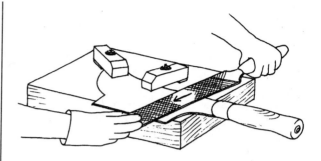

To check if the tool is sharp, hold it up to the light and look along the edge. Any points where light is reflected will indicate where the edge is still a little flat and needs further work. The edge is sharp when no points reflect light. Do not test by using your fingers.

When the edge is well honed, you may find that there is a burr, or very thin leaf of metal, which is left standing on the edge, because it is thin enough to bend and flow under the onslaught of the stone. It can be removed by taking alternate strokes each side several times, always driving the stone towards the edge only. Alternatively, rotate a well-wetted stone along the along the sharpening bevel, first on one side and then on the other. Do this sparingly, as each time it is done the shoulders are thickened slightly which hastens the need for regrinding. Taking a very slightly over obtuse angle on the final strokes with the fine stone also helps.

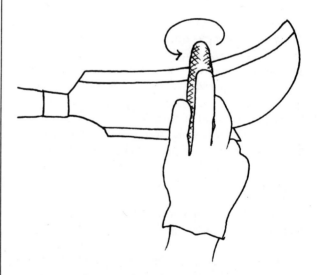

The bluntest part of a billhook is usually near the tip, mainly because this is the most used part. Don't spend hours on the handle end and then skimp the tip. The blade should be sharp along its whole length, and particularly where it is most used.

Billhooks can be quickly blunted by improper use. Ensure that users are trained not to drive billhooks into the ground, nor into gritty surfaces, and that use of billhooks on dead wood is avoided as much as possible, as this dulls the edge.

Scythes and grasshooks

If the blade of a long-handled or 'Turk' scythe needs a major sharpening job, it is safest to remove the blade from the snaith or handle, and clamp it in a jig. Use a flat file to remove any large burrs, and then with a medium or fine cigar stone, hone the curved blade carefully along its whole length, using small circular strokes. Only the upper edge of the blade is sharpened. A grasshook is sharpened in the same way.

Scythes and grasshooks need frequent honing in the field, if they are to cut efficiently, and almost as much time should be spent honing as cutting. To hone a scythe, wedge the end of the snaith firmly on the ground, and steady the back of the blade with the left forearm and hand. Sharpen with your right hand, using a fine cigar stone, stroking away from the edge. Wear gloves on both hands whilst sharpening.

Grasshooks should be honed in the field by holding the tool downwards with the blade facing away from you, and then sharpen with a diagonal movement, away from the blade.

Axes

To sharpen an axe, use a round axe stone either gripped with thumb and fingers around the rim of the stone, or cupped in the palm of the hand. Starting with the medium side of the stone, sharpen with a circular grinding motion, about half the diameter of the stone. Finish with the fine side of the stone. Axes are usually round-cheeked, so work carefully to preserve this shape and the edge angle.

Spades, shovels and hoes

Spades and hoes can get blunt from use in stony soils, and shovels show wear and damage along the blade in normal use.

If badly nicked, briefly grind using a bench- or angle grinder, taking care not to overheat the edge. Alternatively, hold the tool firmly in a vice, and use a medium grade file to sharpen both sides of the blade evenly. Don't overdo it, as a very sharp edge is not needed

Mattocks and pickaxes

Grind worn or damaged tools using a bench grinder or angle grinder . Keep the angle fairly obtuse, and don't try to achieve a 'sharp' edge.

sharpen this blade equally on both sides
sharpen this blade on this face only

Crowbars & wrecking bars

These are made of very hard steel, and any workshop maintenance is difficult. The pointed end of a crowbar, while not sharp, should have a sufficient point to break up rocks, hard ground and so on. The crow end requires a hard edge and sound jaws for effective levering. Grind as necessary using a bench grinder or angle grinder. Badly worn bars can be taken to a blacksmith for re-forging.

Wood chisels

Chisels need to be very sharp, so use an extra fine stone such as a flat carborundum stone. Lay it flat on the bench, and at right angles to the body. Use a light cutting oil to lubricate and provide the cutting medium. The chisel initially abrades away a small amount of stone which combines with the oil to, in turn, abrade away the blade. The chisel is held at a set angle, usually 25 degrees for the backing edge, and 30 degrees for the cutting edge.

CHISEL EDGES

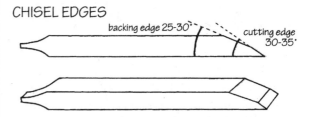
backing edge 25-30° / cutting edge 30-35°

To get the angle correct, it is worth purchasing a honing guide, which is a small tool that clamps onto the chisel and holds it at the required angle. Grasp the chisel in the right hand, with the forefinger pressing down on the flat of the steel. The motion is straight back and forth, towards and away from yourself.

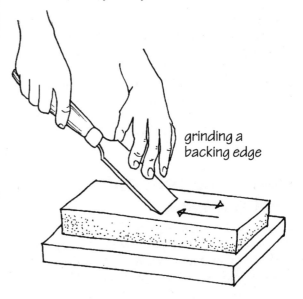
grinding a backing edge

Work gradually over the whole surface of the stone, to avoid hollows forming. Only the oblique side of the blade is honed. Take care to hone the end square. It is easy to press slightly harder on one side of the chisel than the other, by placing the forefinger off-centre, which results in one corner being ground too hard and a cutting edge not square to the axis.

Honing will raise a metal burr on the back of the blade, which is then removed by reversing the chisel so that the back is resting flat on the stone. A short, circular rubbing motion will remove the burr.

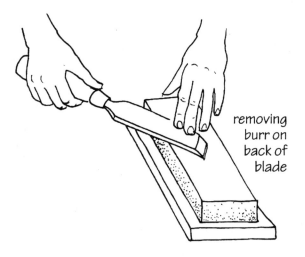

removing burr on back of blade

In extreme cases, where a chip has been taken out of the cutting edge, or where the cutting edge is no longer square to the rest of the blade, regrinding will be necessary. This can be done using a coarse oil stone in the method described above, but is hard and long work. A water-cooled sandstone grinder makes the job a lot easier. An adjustable tool rest can be used to hold the chisel at the correct angle to the grinding wheel. Use very light pressure as the chisel is moved to and fro across the wheel so grinding the blade evenly, and giving even wear on the stone.

If using a grinder that is not water-cooled, great care must be taken not to overheat the end of the chisel or it will lose its temper, i.e. become soft and no longer hold an edge. After two or three seconds of grinding the chisel should be dipped in cold water for a few seconds. Then inspect the blade, and repeat as necessary.

After grinding, the blade should be sharpened as described above.

Bolsters, cold chisels and wedges

These tools are made from extremely hard steel, and sharpening them may prove difficult. They are not designed to cut, but to split and fracture, and although they need not be sharp, some edge is needed.

Wedges are often required to travel beyond their length into the wood. Therefore ensure they have no shoulders to cause an obstruction. It may be possible to remove a

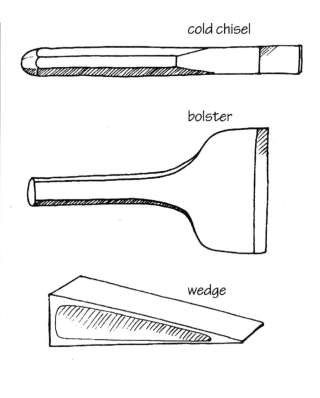

cold chisel

bolster

wedge

shoulder with a file, but it is much easier and quicker with a bench grinder, although care must be taken not to damage the temper of the tool.

For a plastic or wooden wedge, use a file or surform to remove the shoulder.

The edges on cold chisels and bolsters should be made up with a bench grinder. A file is unlikely to have much effect. Also grind to remove any sharp shoulders which develop on the head of the tool. Badly 'mushroomed' tools are dangerous to use, as the hammer can slip off the mushroom head, and chips or steel splinters break off.

mushroomed head

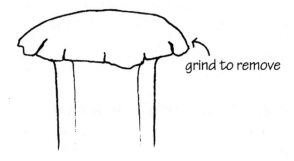

grind to remove

It is possible to buy larger cold chisels and bolsters with plastic hand protectors fitted. Their advantage must be weighed against the fact that the protector makes it difficult to grind the head of the tool. Normally these tools should be used with a gloved hand, which offers some protection.

Secateurs and loppers

Secateurs and loppers can be sharpened without being dismantled. Anvil blades should have both edges of the cutting blade sharpened, whereas only the outer edges of the cutting blade on bypass secateurs or loppers should be sharpened.

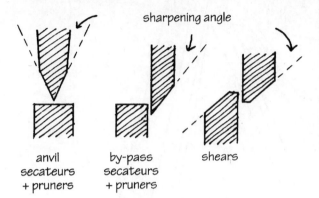

anvil
secateurs
+ pruners

by-pass
secateurs
+ pruners

shears

Before sharpening, any hardened sap residue on the blades should be cleaned with a plastic scouring pad and white spirit. Most loppers can be opened wide and laid on the bench or held in a vice for sharpening. Secateurs, which don't open wide, are more easily held in the left hand for sharpening with the right, using a small circular action with the stone. Start with a

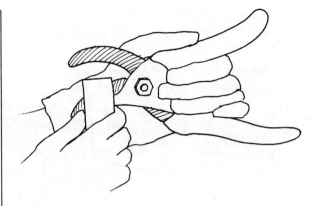

medium grade flat stone, and finish with a fine stone.

Tighten the blades if necessary, by adjusting the centre screw and locknut. Do not overtighten as this makes them difficult to use. Test by cutting a piece of paper. Sharp and well adjusted blades will cut paper easily along the whole length of the blade.

Shears

Hold the shears in a vice. With a medium flat stone, sharpen evenly along the whole length of the blade. Sharpen only the outer edges of the blades, keeping to the original angle. The inner surfaces should remain flat and only need cleaning.

49

SAW SHARPENING HORSE
made from joinery grade planed red deal

frames A + B: 50 x 32mm timber
all joints secured with no.8 screws

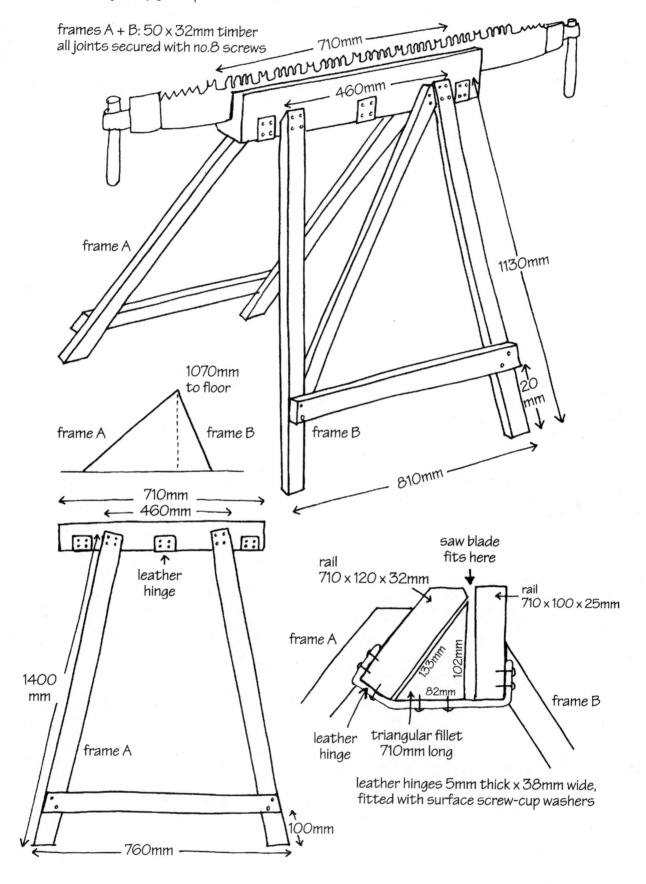

710mm

460mm

1130mm

20 mm

frame A

810mm

1070mm
to floor

frame A   frame B   frame B

710mm
460mm

leather
hinge

saw blade
fits here

rail
710 x 120 x 32mm

rail
710 x 100 x 25mm

frame A

133mm

102mm

82mm

frame B

1400
mm

frame A

leather
hinge

triangular fillet
710mm long

leather hinges 5mm thick x 38mm wide,
fitted with surface screw-cup washers

100mm

760mm

7 Miscellaneous repairs

Wheelbarrows

Wheelbarrows should give years of service, provided they are used and stored properly. They must be stored upright or turned over in dry conditions, and never left holding damp items, or where they can catch rainwater or condensation.

Most main frames are made of tubular steel, and are far stronger than the rest of the barrow. Frames do not easily go out of alignment, but will show some signs of rust after many years of service. Check the handles for cuts or burrs that might catch unwary fingers.

The weak points of most barrows are the sheet steel struts that connect the front of the body to the main frame at the wheel bearings. These easily bend or break, allowing the body to shift forward until the wheel rubs against it. Stronger replacement struts can be made from angle iron, or mild steel tube with the ends flattened, bent over and drilled.

The wheelbarrow body is usually made of sheet steel, and is susceptible to rust. Paint the outside as required, preferably using 'Berlin Black' paint, and oil the inside of the body once a month. The body is attached to the frame either by spot-welds or nuts and bolts. Check that welds are intact, or nuts and bolts are tight.

Holes in the body can be repaired by riveting on sheet metal patches, provided the body is still basically sound.

Wheelbarrows have either solid or pneumatic tyres. Though more expensive and liable to puncture, pneumatic tyres are recommended as they are much easier to use in muddy conditions. Fitting a strip of old carpet inside a tyre can help prevent punctures. Most pneumatic tyres are neoprene, rather than rubber, and quite thin. The carpet helps prevent thorns and other sharp objects penetrating through to the inner tube.

The wheel is usually held on by two cast iron bearings bolted to the main frame. Cast iron is fragile, so do not overtighten the bolts, or attempt to free the bearings with a hammer. Oil the bolts regularly to ensure they do not rust up and so make removal difficult.

Ropes

For storage and coiling of ropes, see page 26.

Ropes used for tree work should be kept separate from ropes used for general work, which may include pond work, hauling wheelbarrows, towing vehicles and so on. Ropes can be distinguished by marking them with fabric dye. Mix up a quantity of cold water dye, suitable for the type of rope, and dip a section of rope into it.

Natural-fibre ropes are still available made of sisal or manila (hemp), but are generally less strong and more liable to rot than man-made fibre ropes. Ropes of man-made fibre are, in order of strength, made of nylon, polyester (Terylene) or polypropylene (see table below).

According to the way they are made, ropes are either hawser-laid (cabled) or kernmantel. Hawser-laid ropes have fibres twisted together to make strands, and then three strands twisted together to make the rope. They can easily kink and require careful coiling. Kernmantel ropes, made of polyester, have a large number of filaments running straight down the rope, encased in a braided sheath. They have a high tensile strength and are non-kinking. Kernmantel ropes for tree work have low stretch. Kernmantel ropes designed for rock climbing have very high stretch and should never be used for tree work.

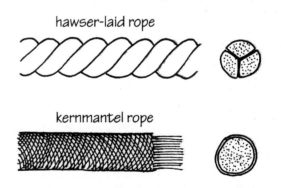

hawser-laid rope

kernmantel rope

Hawser-laid polypropylene ropes are the type most commonly used for conservation work. Although these do not rot in water, they should still be stored dry and away from chemicals and batteries. Polypropylene ropes float, which is an advantage for pond work. Hawser-laid sisal or manila ropes will rot if kept damp.

If ropes are returned to the store very muddy, they should be washed, coiled loosely to dry and then coiled for storage. All ropes should be checked once a month for damage and wear by uncoiling them and making a careful visual check.

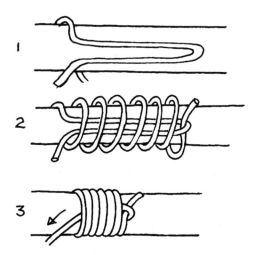

Very badly frayed or damaged ropes should be discarded. Ropes with one or more points of damage can be cut and the sound lengths kept for general purposes. Singe the ends of man-made fibre ropes to seal them. Use fine string (whipping twine) to whip the ends of natural-fibre ropes, as shown above.

The table below gives the breaking load and safe working load of various sizes and types of rope.

Table 7.1

ROPE (diam.)	BREAKING LOAD (kg)	SAFE WORKING LOAD (kg)
Sisal 8mm	480	80
Sisal 12mm	950	158
Sisal 16mm	1780	296
Sisal 24mm	4060	676
Manila 8mm	540	90
Manila 12mm	1070	178
Manila 16mm	2030	338
Manila 24mm	4570	761
Polypropylene 8mm	960	160
Polypropylene 12mm	2030	383
Polypropylene 16mm	3500	583
Polypropylene 24mm	7600	1266
Polyester 12mm	3000	500
Nylon 10mm	2080	346
Nylon 12mm	3000	500
Nylon 14mm	4100	683

Bowsaws

Bowsaws are available in various shapes and sizes, from 530mm (21") to 900m (36"). A bowsaw is essentially a frame which pulls a disposable blade under tension.

The frames are made of steel tube, either circular or oval in cross section. Frames with plastic hand guards are recommended. Check the frame for burrs, and ensure tension levers are secure. The holes for rivets and studs should be clear of mud, wood and other debris.

Tensioning on most saws is by lever operation. Oil the pivot of the lever occasionally to ensure smooth operation and secure fastening. Some saws have no levers, but are sprung to tension the blade. Depending on age and type of saw, the blade is fixed either by a tongue, a rivet or nut and bolt. A tongue fixing is preferable, as rivets, nuts and bolts are easily lost. If the tongue breaks, rather than throw the saw away, a hole can be drilled for a small nut and bolt to secure the blade. Any saw that cannot hold a blade under tension should be discarded, although it may be possible to restore the tension by holding the saw in a vice and bending the ends apart slightly. Frames keep their tension longer if they are stored with the tension released.

Blades usually lose their set before becoming blunt, by being trapped in the felling cuts of trees. This makes them bind in future cuts, giving the impression that they must be blunt. The blade can be given a new set by gripping it in the vice up to the base of the teeth, and then tweaking each tooth in turn to the correct side, using a pair of fencing pliers. Grip the tooth below the hardened tip or it will break off. Although not a very accurate method, it is effective and gives the blade a new lease of life. Blades are not worth resharpening.

When not in use, the saw blade should be protected with a plastic guard.

Crosscut saws

Two-person crosscut saws can vary in length from about 1.2m (4') to 1.8m (6') in length, with blade depths from 150mm (6") to 230mm (9"). The pattern of the teeth is either peg, or four peg and raker. The saws can be set using either a hammer and anvil, or a plier type saw set. The four peg and raker saw can be sharpened with a normal triangular saw file, but the peg tooth saw must be sharpened with a narrow-cant saw file.

Hold the file horizontally and at an angle of 60-70 degrees to the blade. Unlike other saws, the teeth on two person crosscut saws are filed both front and back, so that the saw cuts on both strokes.

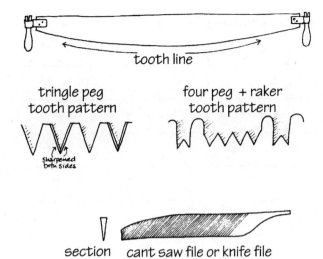

tooth line

tringle peg
tooth pattern

four peg + raker
tooth pattern

sharpened
both sides

section   cant saw file or knife file

On a blunt saw, the points of the teeth appear slightly rounded on close examination. The sharpening process forms the teeth to points, and removes the rounded bright spots on the tooth points. When filing, only remove the minimum of metal, just enough to bring the teeth to a point. Do not forget to take down the raker teeth as necessary. Saw sharpening is a skill that takes time and practice to acquire.

Setting and sharpening a two-person crosscut saw is best done with the saw held in a special sharpening horse, the design of which is shown on page 50.

Alternatively, the saw can be held between two planks of wood clamped between two vices.

When not in use, grease or oil the blades and hang the saws up.

Winches

Details of the safe operation and maintenance of Tirfor winches is given in a booklet available from Tractel (UK) Ltd., Old Lane, Halfway, Sheffield S20 3GA (Tel: 0114 248 2266).

Winches should be inspected, cleaned and lubricated at regular intervals. At least annually, they should be thoroughly examined by a competent person, usually a Tirfor dealer. Contact the manufacturers for the address of your nearest repairer. Never try to take a winch apart, as it contains extremely powerful springs. Slings, wire rope and other accessories should also be examined before each use, and subjected to the same examination routine as the winch.

The winch has shear pins which are designed to break if the load is too heavy, to prevent damage to the winch. Always keep a spare stock of pins.

Cables should be stored carefully (p24).

Waders and wellies

Waders and wellies are worth repairing if ripped or punctured, but not if general deterioration has set in. To repair holes and tears, buy sufficient patch strip and rubber solvent adhesive from a bicycle repair shop. Use fine sandpaper to roughen the rubber around the hole so that the adhesive will bond. Note that non-rubber wellies cannot be repaired this way.

Monkey strainers

Replacement springs and rivets can be obtained. Check with your local supplier of agricultural or fencing equipment.

Safety equipment

Helmets

Any safety helmets purchased should be in accordance with EN 397. It is a good idea to purchase a different colour for each year, so their age can be easily seen. In addition, date of purchase can be marked on the inside of the helmet, by writing on the manufacturer's label with a waterproof pen. Do not write directly onto the helmet, as the solvents in the pen can weaken the helmet fabric. Similarly, never paint the outside of a helmet. Store helmets out of direct sunlight, as sunlight degrades them.

Check helmets regularly, and discard any with obvious signs of damage. Any helmets which are known to have received heavy impact should also be discarded. Helmet manufacturers recommend that all helmets should be changed every two years.

First aid kits

First aid kits should be stored in a strong container with a properly fitting lid. Kits are available from BTCV Enterprises Limited (address on page 2).

The first aid container should be sealed with an adhesive label showing the date the contents were checked and restocked. After each use the kit should be restocked and a new seal attached.

See overleaf for contents of a 10 person kit:

A kit suitable for use in a workplace for up to 10 people, should contain the following: :

Guidance card	1
Waterproof plasters	20
Sterile eye pads, with attachment	2
Individually wrapped triangular bandages	6
Safety pins	6
Extra large lint dressings	3
Medium sterile dressings (12cm x 12cm)	6
Large sterile dressings (18cm x 18cm)	2
Alcohol free cleansing wipes	6
Scissors	1
Pairs of fine transparent disposable plastic gloves	2

NOTE: Where mains tap water is not readily available for eye irrigation, sterile water or sterile normal saline (0.9%) in sealed disposable containers should be provided. Each container should hold at least 300ml and should not be reused once the sterile seal is broken. At least 900ml should be provided. Eye baths or other refillable containers should not be used for eye irrigation.*

*A wall-mounted Eye Wash Station with eye wash solution, eye pads and mirror is available from BTCV Enterprises Limited.

Further reading

Batsford (1999)
   Traditional woodworking handtools
   Graham Blackburn

David and Charles (1994)
   John Sainsbury's Home Workshop
   John Sainsbury

Guild of Master Craftsmen Publications Ltd. (1996)
   Sharpening – pocket reference book
   Jim Kingshott

Index